California Treasures

Practice Book

Macmillan/McGraw-Hill

The McGraw·Hill Companies

 Macmillan
McGraw-Hill

Published by Macmillan/McGraw-Hill, of McGraw-Hill Education, a division of The McGraw-Hill Companies, Inc.,
Two Penn Plaza, New York, New York 10121.

Printed in the United States of America

11 ROV 15

Contents

Unit 1 • Let's Learn

Contents

Unit 2 • Neighborhoods and Communities

Contents

Unit 3 • Express Yourself

Contents

Unit 4 • Our Teams

Contents

Unit 5 • Those Amazing Animals

Contents

Unit 6 • Storytellers

Name _____

The **short vowel** sounds are the vowel sounds that the letters
a, e, i, o, and *u* stand for in the following words:

pack   step   pick   sock   truck

Fill the blank in each word below with a vowel letter. You should make a word with a short vowel sound that makes sense in the sentence.

1. Please st_____p to the rear of the bus.

2. Our new baby sleeps in a cr_____b.

3. This is the first time I have eaten carrots for a sn_____ck.

4. I just learned how to j_____mp rope.

5. Our first time at the park we saw ducks in the p_____nd.

6. Sandy forgot to put a st_____mp on the first letter she wrote.

7. The audience will cl_____p at the beginning of the show.

8. Mom and Dad will sh_____p for a new car.

9. I have to p_____ck my clothes before I leave.

10. Pat will p_____ck the place to go on vacation.

11. My room was a m_____ss after my little brother played in it.

12. Would you like a peach or a pl_____m?

CA **R 1.1** Know and use complex word families when reading (e.g., *-ight*)
to decode unfamiliar words.

Name _____

Use the clues to complete the following crossword puzzle.

| trudged | nonsense | nervous |
| fumbled | downstairs | chuckled |

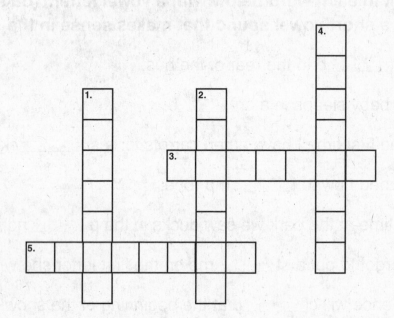

Across

3. did something in a clumsy way

5. laughed in a quiet way

Down

1. afraid or worried

2. walked slowly

4. silly or untrue idea

CA R 1.0 Word Analysis, Fluency, and Systematic Vocabulary Development

Name _____

The **characters** are the people or animals in a story. The **plot** includes the important events that happen in the beginning, middle, and end of the story. The **setting** is when and where the story happens.

Read the story, then answer the questions below.

At 9:00 A.M. on his first day of work at the supermarket, Josh was given shopping cart duty. It was cold out, and Josh did not want this task, but he was a good worker.

Josh started his search for carts by walking up and down the supermarket parking lot. He started a train of shopping carts, and after an hour Josh had twenty-five carts. He pushed them all into the front of the store.

Josh was about to go out for more carts when his boss called out to him, "Hold on there, Josh. You're such a good worker that we are making you a cashier. Come on in, and start your training."

1. When does this story take place?

_____

2. Where does this story take place?

_____

3. Who is the main character in this story? How can you tell?

_____

4. What is the first important event in this story?

_____

5. What is the last important event in this story?

_____

© Macmillan/McGraw-Hill

R 3.2 Comprehend basic plots of classic fairy tales, myths, folktales, legends, and fables from around the world.
R 3.3 Determine what characters are like by what they say or do and by how the author or illustrator portrays them.

First Day Jitters • Grade 3/Unit 1   **11**

As you read *First Day Jitters*, fill in the Story Map.

Characters

Setting

Beginning

Middle

End

How does the information you wrote in this Story Map help you analyze story structure in *First Day Jitters*?

CA   **R 3.2** Comprehend basic plots of classic fairy tales, myths, folktales, legends, and fables from around the world.
R 3.3 Determine what characters are like by what they say or do and by how the author or illustrator portrays them.

As I read, I will pay attention to phrasing.

	One Monday in November, Jay and his mother drove
9	to a yellow brick building with a sign in front that said:
21	"Rosewood Middle School." It was a big building—much
30	taller than Jay's old school.
35	Jay's mother filled out lots of forms. Before they left,
45	the school principal, Ms. Tucker, came out of her office
55	and shook Jay's hand. "Welcome to Rosewood," she said.
64	"We'll see you tomorrow."
68	On Tuesday morning, Jay's older sister, Eva, gave him
77	a ride to school. "Are you nervous?" she asked.
86	Jay shrugged and then nodded. "I hate being the new kid,"
97	he admitted. 99

Comprehension Check

1. Who is the main character, and what is the story about? **Plot Development**

2. Why is Jay nervous? **Plot Development**

	Words Read	−	Number of Errors	=	Words Correct Score
First Read		−		=	
Second Read		−		=	

R 1.3 Read aloud narrative and expository text fluently and accurately and with appropriate pacing, intonation, and expression.

Name _____

Look at a **bar graph** to compare the numbers represented by the bars. The title tells what the graph is about. Labels tell you what each row is about. The numbers show amounts.

Use the bar graph to answer the questions below.

How Did You Feel on Your First Day of School?

Feelings on First Day of School

1. Most of the students said they felt _____.
   a. afraid   **b.** curious

2. Four students said they felt _____.
   a. happy   **b.** afraid

3. The total number of students that felt either happy or curious was _____.
   a. 10   **b.** 2

4. More students felt _____ than _____.
   a. afraid, excited   **b.** excited, happy

5. You can use the graph to find out _____.
   a. how many more students felt happy than excited
   b. why more students felt curious than afraid

© Macmillan/McGraw-Hill

CA **R 2.1** Use titles, tables of contents, chapter headings, glossaries, and indexes to locate information in text.

Name _____

The **prefixes** *un-* and *non-* are word parts that can be added to the beginning of base words. They form new words with new meanings. *Un-* means "not" or "the opposite of." *Non-* means "not" or "without."

un + kind = unkind   *non + stop = nonstop*

**Add the prefix *un-* or *non-* to the words in the box.
Then complete the sentences below with the new words.**

_____ usual	_____ happy	_____ safe
_____ stick	_____ wrap	_____ skid

1. We learn to make _____ foods in cooking class.

2. First, the teacher may _____ the ingredients.

3. We usually cook in _____ pans.

4. The kitchen floor is covered with _____ mats.

5. Without the mats, the kitchen could be _____.

6. I would be _____ to miss cooking class.

R 1.8 Use knowledge of **prefixes** (e.g., *un-, re-, pre-, bi-, mis-, dis-*)
and **suffixes** (e.g., *-er, -est, -ful*) to determine the meaning of words.

Name _____

Using the Word Study Steps

1. LOOK at the word.

2. SAY the word aloud.

3. STUDY the letters in the word.

4. WRITE the word.

5. CHECK the word.
   Did you spell the word right?
   If not, go back to step 1.

Find Rhyming Words

Circle the word in each row that rhymes with the word in dark type.

1. **sock**	truck	rock	sick
2. **dress**	mess	dust	mast
3. **trap**	track	clam	clap
4. **bump**	jump	junk	bunch
5. **fed**	hid	head	hide
6. **pick**	sick	sock	dock
7. **ramp**	fan	sand	stamp
8. **back**	snap	sneak	snack
9. **top**	tip	crib	crop
10. **brick**	clock	click	cluck
11. **kiss**	miss	mist	mask
12. **cut**	shut	cat	sat
13. **duck**	dark	luck	lark
14. **pep**	pop	step	stop
15. **bond**	plod	plop	pond

© Macmillan/McGraw-Hill

LC 1.8 Spell correctly one-syllable words that have blends, contractions, compounds, orthographic patterns (e.g., *qu*, consonant doubling, changing the ending of a word from -*y* to -*ies* when forming the plural), and common homophones (e.g., *hair-hare*).

Name _____

A. There are six spelling mistakes in the drama club flyer. Circle the misspelled words. Write the words correctly on the lines.

Join the drama club! You can stepp up on stage and be a star! All of your friends are doing it, and now so can you.

When you join the drama club, you will enter a new world. You can pretend to be anything. Be a cat, and gump on a mouse. Be an old frog on a roc in the middle of a ponnd. The only limit is your imagination.

Everyone is scared at first, but the only way to get over your fears is to try. With any lukk, when you walk off the stage, the people watching will clapp until their hands hurt.

The drama club is a great way to make new friends. Come and find the actor inside you. Join us!

1. _____   4. _____

2. _____   5. _____

3. _____   6. _____

Writing Activity

B. Write a postcard to an old friend describing your first day of school. Use at least four spelling words in your description.

_____

_____

_____

_____

_____

_____

LC 1.8 Spell correctly one-syllable words that have blends, contractions, compounds, orthographic patterns (e.g., *qu*, consonant doubling, changing the ending of a word from -*y* to -*ies* when forming the plural), and common homophones (e.g., *hair-hare*).

First Day Jitters • **Grade 3/Unit 1**   **17**

Name _____

- A **statement** is a sentence that tells something. It ends with a period.
- A **question** is a sentence that asks something. It ends with a question mark.
  Statement: There are many ways to make new friends.
  Question: What do you do to make friends?

Write *statement* if the sentence tells something. Write *question* if the sentence asks something. Put the correct end mark at the end of the sentence.

1. Meg liked to make new friends _____

2. She said hello to the new student _____

3. How would you greet a new student _____

4. She told him about their school _____

5. She told him how they had fun _____

6. What would you say about your school _____

7. She showed him around the school _____

8. Where would you take a new student _____

9. What would you ask someone new _____

10. Do you like to hear about new places _____

11. We like our school _____

12. What was your school like _____

13. We have a lot of fun reading _____

14. Have fun at your new school _____

© Macmillan/McGraw-Hill

LC 1.1 Understand and be able to use complete and correct declarative, interrogative, imperative, and exclamatory sentences in writing and speaking.

Name _____

- A sentence is a group of words that tells a complete thought.
- A **statement** is a sentence that tells something.
- A **question** is a sentence that asks something.

Read the description of Carly's first day at camp. Circle the mistakes, and rewrite the paragraph.

I woke up early. it was the first day of camp. I didn't know what to expect. Would I know anyone in my group. Would we do things I like to do? Would we swim in the lake or the pool? I've never gone swimming outside before!

The bus was already filled with campers. I looked nervously down the aisle? Then I saw Lisa. she had been on my soccer team. I sat down next to her. Now I didn't even mind the rain. It would be fine because I had a friend with me.

_____

_____

_____

_____

_____

_____

_____

_____

LC 1.1 Understand and be able to use complete and correct declarative, interrogative, imperative, and exclamatory sentences in writing and speaking.
LC 1.0 Written and Oral English Language Conventions

First Day Jitters • **Grade 3/Unit 1** 19

1. Please read the following passage.

   Shawn and Kathy were on the basketball court. Cindy was flying a kite in the field. Sitting under a tree, Jon, Latoya, and Abe ate their lunch.

2. Underline one sentence.

3. Now, write two more sentences about that sentence.

Example: <u>Cindy was flying a kite in the field.</u> She held on to the string as tight as she could and ran in a zig-zag back and forth on the grass. As she ran, she giggled so loudly that everyone could hear her from across the field.

_____

_____

_____

_____

_____

_____

_____

_____

Extra Practice: Do the same activity with one of the other sentences.

CA W 1.0 Writing Strategies

A final silent **e** often makes the vowel in that syllable have the long vowel sound. For example:

conf**use**   ref**ine**   disl**ike**   panc**ake**   al**one**   qu**ote**

Circle the word that has a long vowel sound and a final silent e. Then write it on the line to complete the sentence.

1. We read a book about a storm called a _____.

rainstorm   blizzard   hurricane

2. We looked at a _____ to see where one can form.

map   globe   book

3. We learned when a hurricane might _____.

begin   appear   arrive

4. We found out the storm can bring _____ winds.

high   brisk   huge

5. The amount of rain can _____ you.

surprise   surround   frighten

6. Scientists can _____ how strong the storm will be.

complain   compute   tell

7. No two storms are exactly _____.

always   similar   alike

8. Our class _____ a report about hurricanes.

read   printed   wrote

CA **R 1.2** Decode regular multisyllabic words.

Name _____

Read the story. Choose words from the box to complete the sentences. Then write the answers on the lines.

auditions	adventure	exploring	sparkling	fantastic	success

My friends and I love _____ stories. We wish we could go _____ with the story characters. We can't do that. But we do learn all sorts of things from these exciting tales.

Sometimes we put on a play about a story we're reading. We hold _____ to see who will play each part. From the book, we learn where and when the story takes place. Then we take old clothes and add decorations like _____ jewels to make costumes. We make the costumes look like clothes the story characters wore. People who see our plays often say the costumes are _____. The right costumes help make a play a _____.

CA R 1.0 Word Analysis, Fluency, and Systematic Vocabulary Development

Name _____

The **cause** is what makes something happen. The **effect** is what happens as a result.

Write a sentence that tells the missing cause or effect.

1. Cause: Our library needed to raise money to buy new books and equipment.

   Effect: _____

   _____

2. Cause: _____

   _____

   Effect: We raised over $200.00 for the library book fund.

3. Cause: The library bought two new computers.

   Effect: _____

   _____

4. Cause: I took a computer class after school.

   Effect: _____

   _____

© Macmillan/McGraw-Hill

R 2.6 Extract appropriate and significant information from the text, including problems and solutions.

Name _____

As you read *Amazing Grace*, fill in the Cause and Effect Chart.

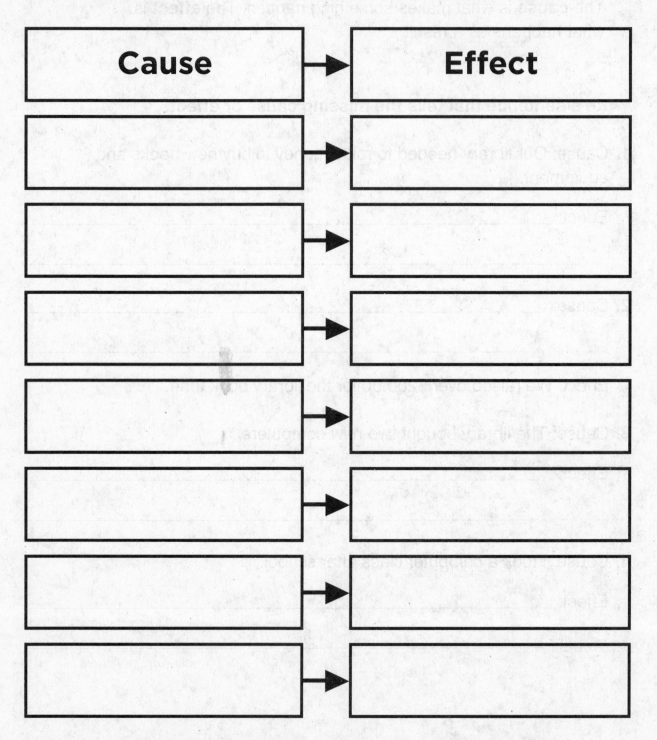

Cause		Effect
	→	
	→	
	→	
	→	
	→	
	→	
	→	

How does the information you wrote in this Cause and Effect Chart
help you retell *Amazing Grace*?

R 2.6 Extract appropriate and significant information from the text,
including problems and solutions.

© Macmillan/McGraw-Hill

Name _____

As I read, I will pay attention to my intonation.

	Rain forests are home to over half the world's plants
10	and animals. When the rain forest is lost, the circle of life
22	breaks down. The climate changes. The plants and animals
31	die off.
33	People have come up with many ways to address this
43	problem. One way to save the forests is to learn all about
55	them.
56	Another way is to get wood from somewhere else. Now
66	there are tree farms where wood is grown. If you can get
78	trees from a farm, then you don't need to cut down a forest.
91	Cutting a rain-forest tree should only be done as a last
102	resort. 103

Comprehension Check

1. What happens when the rain forest is lost? **Main Idea and Details**

2. What are ways to help save the forests? **Main Idea and Details**

	Words Read	–	Number of Errors	=	Words Correct Score
First Read		–		=	
Second Read		–		=	

CA **R 1.3** Read aloud narrative and expository text fluently and accurately and with appropriate pacing, intonation, and expression.

Personification means giving human characteristics to an animal or thing. Examples:

The star raced across the sky.   My old car coughed.

A **legend** is a story that is passed down orally from older people to younger ones. It may teach a lesson or explain why something happens. A legend often includes personification.

Read the legend below. Then answer the questions.

Father Sun and Mother Moon lived inside the rocks at Rock House. They didn't give any light to the sky, so the people and the animals lived in darkness. Coyote loved to play tricks. He thought it would be fun to dump fleas on Father Sun and Mother Moon. He gathered fleas in a bag and set out. On the way, he met Rabbit and Gopher. When he told them his plan, Rabbit and Gopher joined him on the path to Rock House. When they got to Rock House, they dumped the fleas down a hole in the rocks and ran away.

The fleas landed on Father Sun and Mother Moon. Mother Moon flew out of Rock House and began to fly around the Earth. Father Sun followed, racing around the Earth trying to get rid of those fleas. That is why, to this day, the Sun follows the Moon across the sky.

1. How does the author use personification in this legend? _____

_____

_____

2. What is this legend trying to explain? _____

_____

_____

© Macmillan/McGraw-Hill

(CA) **R 3.2** Comprehend basic plots of classic fairy tales, myths, folktales, legends, and fables from around the world.

> A **word family** is a group of words that have the same word part.
> This word part is called the base word. Knowing the meaning
> of the base word can help you figure out the meaning of other
> words in the word family.

**A. Read each sentence below. Circle the word that belongs to
the same word family as the underlined word.**

1. My favorite books are about people who <u>discover</u> places no one has ever
been before.

    a. extra   **b.** like   **c.** recover

2. When you read, you can <u>imagine</u> you're in a faraway place.

    a. interest   **b.** imaginary   **c.** think

**B. Read each sentence below. Write two words that belong to the same
word family as the underlined word.**

3. I would love to take a trip on a <u>houseboat</u>. _____

_____

4. I read a story about a man in a <u>lighthouse</u> who saved hundreds of ships.

_____

_____

5. Have you ever seen a <u>waterfall</u>? _____

_____

6. It's fun to recite silly poems from <u>memory</u>. _____

_____

Name _____

Using the Word Study Steps

1. LOOK at the word.
2. SAY the word aloud.
3. STUDY the letters in the word.
4. WRITE the word.

5. CHECK the word.
   Did you spell the word right?
   If not, go back to step 1.

Choose the spelling word that best completes the sentence.

1. My favorite flower is a _____.

2. We have to fly in a _____ to visit my grandparents.

3. I make sure to put the _____ on the top of my letters.

4. Dave swims in the _____ every summer.

5. I looked at a _____ to see the country where my pen pal was from.

6. Jill saw _____ at the top of the house and knew there was a fire.

7. My favorite meal for dinner is _____ and chicken.

8. My younger sister is in the first _____.

9. I asked my uncle to _____ over to help me with my homework.

10. To live a long _____ , you should exercise and eat healthy food.

11. I wrote my brother a letter to ask him when he was coming _____.

12. My grandfather tells me to always do my homework so I can be _____ when I grow up.

13. I _____ every time I see my new puppy.

14. To be _____ , I look both ways when I cross the street.

15. I felt _____ after a lot of rest.

LC 1.8 Spell correctly one-syllable words that have blends, contractions, compounds, orthographic patterns (e.g., *qu*, consonant doubling, changing the ending of a word from *-y* to *-ies* when forming the plural), and common homophones (e.g., *hair-hare*).

Name _____

A. There are five spelling mistakes in this letter. Circle the misspelled words. Write the words correctly on the lines below.

Dear Aunt Mary,

I am back in Boston! Our plain ride was fun. It was cool to look out the window and see the mountains and clouds. I even saw the layk when we were taking off! The people in those little cars had no idea I was watching them. It was great!

It was great to visit you, but I'm glad to be hoom, saif and sound. We must make sure to talk often. I will try to write you as many letters as I can. Please com and see us soon.

Love,
Margaret

1. _____   4. _____

2. _____   5. _____

3. _____

B. Writing Activity

Write a letter to your friend describing a trip you would like to take. Use at least three spelling words in your description.

_____

_____

_____

_____

LC 1.8 Spell correctly one-syllable words that have blends, contractions, compounds, orthographic patterns (e.g., *qu*, consonant doubling, changing the ending of a word from *-y* to *-ies* when forming the plural), and common homophones (e.g., *hair-hare*).

Amazing Grace • **Grade 3/Unit I**   **29**

- An **exclamation** shows strong feeling. It ends with an exclamation mark.
  Sentence: What great news!

Add a word from the box to make each group of words an exclamation. Then write the sentence correctly.

great	Hey	Look	Quick
see	too	What	Wow

1. _____, there's a letter for you

   _____

2. _____ a surprise

   _____

3. _____, open the envelope

   _____

4. _____, it's from Aunt Cara

   _____

5. _____, she has a new puppy

   _____

6. That's _____

   _____

7. There's a picture, _____

   _____

8. Let me _____

   _____

CA LC 1.1 Understand and be able to use complete and correct declarative, interrogative, imperative, and exclamatory sentences in writing and speaking.

Name _____

- A **command** is a sentence that tells someone to do something.
- An **exclamation** shows strong feeling.

Rewrite the letter from Steve, fixing any mistakes you might find.

Dear Chris,

What great news. I'm so happy to hear that you are coming to visit next month. wow, I can't believe it's been a year since you were last here I already have plans for things to do. I'll give you some hints. Bring your sleeping bag Pack a flashlight. Don't forget the bug spray. yes, we're going camping

I hope you'll do me another favor. Ask your dad for his chocolate chip cookie recipe His cookies are the best! Then I'll practice making them while you are here.

Sincerely yours,
Your favorite cousin,
Steve

_____

_____

_____

_____

_____

_____

_____

LC 1.1 Understand and be able to use complete and correct declarative, interrogative, imperative, and exclamatory sentences in writing and speaking.

Amazing Grace • **Grade 3/Unit I**   **31**

1. Remember when you brushed your teeth this morning.

2. List three actions you took in order to brush your teeth.

a. _____

b. _____

c. _____

3. Now, write three sentences that focus on how you brushed your teeth.

Example: I held my toothbrush under the cold water coming from the tap. Crusty, dried-up toothpaste fell into the sink as I unscrewed the toothpaste cap. I had to squeeze hard from the end of the old tube to get the paste onto my brush.

_____

_____

_____

_____

_____

_____

_____

_____

_____

Extra Practice: Do the same activity for "I tied my shoes."

CA **W 1.0** Writing Strategies

Name _____

When a vowel says its name, it is a long vowel. When a syllable has two vowels, the letters usually stand for the sound of the first vowel. The letters *ai* or *ay* stand for the long *a* sound.

A. Read each sentence. Circle the word that has the long *a* sound.

1. It's fun to walk outside in the rain.

2. I like to paint using watercolors.

3. The kitten plays with yarn until it is tired.

4. "Don't knock over that pail!"

5. May is one of the loveliest months of the year.

6. My dog laid by my feet during dinner.

B. Write rhyming words for each of the words with the long *a* sound.

7. rain _____

8. paint _____

9. plays _____

10. pail _____

11. May _____

12. laid _____

R 1.1 Know and use complex word families when reading (e.g., *-ight*) to decode unfamiliar words.

Earth Smart • **Grade 3/Unit I** 33

Name _____

unaware   members   contribute   donate

A. Use the clues to complete the puzzle with words from the box.

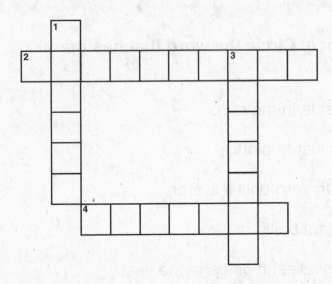

Across

2. to work with a group by giving your time, money, or efforts to achieve a common goal. Example: My class will _____ to the "Green World" program by collecting cans and newspapers for recycling.

4. the people who make up a group

Down

1. to give time or money to help other people. Example: I want to _____ some of my allowance to the local animal shelter.

3. to not know something is happening

B. Write a sentence using one of the vocabulary words.

_____

_____

CA R 1.0 Word Analysis, Fluency, and Systematic Vocabulary Development

> The **main idea** of a paragraph or section is the most important
> idea the writer wants readers to know about. The main idea is
> often stated.
>
> Supporting **details** are examples and evidence that help
> explain the main idea. A paragraph or section may include
> other details that don't support the main idea.

Read the passage. Then answer the questions that follow.

Many people have helped students in their community get an education.
In California, the Major League Baseball organization built baseball fields,
a clubhouse, and a learning center. Kids learn to play baseball, as well
as reading and math. Some kids like football better than baseball. Craig
Kielburger started a group called Free the Children. Free the Children has
built more than 450 schools around the world.

1. What is the main idea of this paragraph? _____

_____

_____

2. Choose two details that tell more about the main idea.

_____

_____

_____

_____

CA R 2.5 Distinguish the main idea and supporting details in expository text.

Earth Smart • Grade 3/Unit I   **35**

As you read *Earth Smart*, fill in the Main Idea and Details Chart.

Main Idea _____

_____

_____

Detail 1 _____

_____

Detail 2 _____

_____

↓

Summary _____

_____

_____

How does the information you wrote in the Main Idea and Details
Chart help you summarize *Earth Smart*?

CA **R 2.5** Distinguish the main idea and supporting details in expository text.

Name _____

As I read, I will pay attention to pacing.

	Charlie called Emma. "I've got a problem," he told her
10	as soon as she picked up the phone. "How can I show my
23	mom I can take care of a pet?"
31	"Hmmm…," said Emma. "What if you did some
39	research on pets?"
42	"Yeah," he said. "I could do that."
49	"Listen," Emma said. "Lucy needs a bath. She keeps
58	scratching her fur, and I'm worried that she has fleas. Let's
69	talk about this tomorrow, okay?"
74	Charlie called Josh. Josh said, "I can't talk. I'm feeding
84	Prince. I can't believe this dog's appetite! If I don't get this
96	food in his bowl, I'm afraid he's going to cook for himself." 108

Comprehension Check

1. What is Charlie's problem? **Problem and Solution**

2. Why can't Charlie's friends talk with him about his problem? **Plot**

	Words Read	–	Number of Errors	=	Words Correct Score
First Read		–		=	
Second Read		–		=	

© Macmillan/McGraw-Hill

CA R 1.3 Read aloud narrative and expository text fluently and accurately
and with appropriate pacing, intonation, and expression.

Earth Smart • Grade 3/Unit I   37

- A dictionary lists **entry words** in alphabetical order. Words that begin with the same letter are alphabetized according to their second or third letter. **Guide words** at the top of the page show the first and last words found on that page.
- Entry words are printed in bold type and are often shown divided into syllables. The **pronunciation** for each word is shown. A **definition** is given for each meaning of a word. There may be a sentence to show how to use the word.

Study the dictionary pages below. Then answer the questions.

132 **green/grove**

green (grēn) 1. the color of grass; 2. not ripe; 3. not harmful to the environment: *Electric cars are more green than gas-powered cars.*

grow/guide 133

grow (grō) 1.to get larger, increase; 2.to get older; 3. to raise: *We grow wheat on our farm.*

1. What is the first entry word on page 132? _____

2. How many definitions are given for *green*? _____

3. Which definition best fits the way *green* is used in the sample sentence?

_____

4. What is the last entry word on p. 133? _____

5. Which entry word would appear on p. 132—*great* or *ground*?

_____

CA W 1.3 Understand the structure and organization of various reference materials (e.g., dictionary, thesaurus, atlas, encyclopedia).

Name _____

Description Writing Frame

A. Summarize "Earth Smart." Use the Description Writing Frame below.

The Goodwillie Environmental School is a green school. The students at this green school help the environment in **many ways**.

One way they help is _____

_____

_____

_____ .

Another way they help is _____

_____

_____

_____ .

They also help by _____

_____

_____

_____ .

B. Rewrite the completed summary on another sheet of paper. Keep it as a model for writing a summary of an article or selection using this text structure.

A **thesaurus** is a book of synonyms. **Synonyms** are words that have similar meanings. When you don't know the exact meaning of a word, finding words with similar meanings in a thesaurus can help you figure out the meaning of that word. Sometimes a word has more than one meaning. A thesaurus will provide synonyms for each meaning of the word.

A. Read the thesaurus entry. Then answer the question below.

direction 1. leadership, guidance, control, management
2. guideline, instruction, rule, order, command **3.** path, route, course, track, way.

1. How many different meanings of **direction** does this thesaurus entry

   provide? _____

B. Use the thesaurus entry to find a synonym for *direction* that makes sense in each sentence. Write a synonym.

2. Our school is under the *direction* of our new principal, Mrs. Jackson.

   _____

3. Which *direction* do you want to take on our hike? _____

4. Did you read the *directions* before you started the activity?

   _____

CA R 1.4 Use knowledge of antonyms, synonyms, homophones, and homographs to determine the meaning of words.

Name _____

Using the Word Study Steps

1. LOOK at the word.

2. SAY the word aloud.

3. STUDY the letters in the word.

4. WRITE the word.

5. CHECK the word.
   Did you spell the word right?
   If not, go back to step 1.

Find and Circle

Where are the spelling words?

P	L	A	I	N	M	P	L	A	Y	S	O	E	H
A	B	R	A	I	D	A	G	R	E	A	T	S	F
I	A	T	S	K	C	I	R	A	Y	A	R	U	A
N	Y	S	N	A	I	L	A	N	P	M	A	Y	I
T	R	A	I	L	D	J	Y	S	W	A	Y	V	L

© Macmillan/McGraw-Hill

LC 1.8 Spell correctly one-syllable words that have blends,
contractions, compounds, orthographic patterns (e.g., *qu*, consonant
doubling, changing the ending of a word from -*y* to -*ies* when forming
the plural), and common homophones (e.g., *hair-hare*).

Earth Smart • Grade 3/Unit 1   41

Name _____

A. There are eight spelling mistakes in this paragraph. Circle the misspelled words. Write the words correctly on the lines below.

Every Mai I visit my grandma. She moved near the bae two years
ago, but it already feels like home. It is a fun place to live. I always bring
my payl and I fill it with sand and sometimes a snale gets in there. We
sometimes have visitors. On nice days the seagulls fly over her house. I
throw them bread crumbs and give them names.

My grandma plase lots of card games with me. She also teaches me a
few card tricks. Sometimes we peant pictures of the trees in her yard.

After dinners we take walks on a trayl by the water. The sky is gray,
the air is cool, and the sounds of the bay fill the night.

It is grait to visit grandma.

1. _____   5. _____

2. _____   6. _____

3. _____   7. _____

4. _____   8. _____

B. Writing Activity

**Write about a place you like to visit. Use at least three spelling
words in your description.**

_____

_____

_____

_____

_____

LC 1.8 Spell correctly one-syllable words that have blends,
contractions, compounds, orthographic patterns (e.g., *qu*, consonant
doubling, changing the ending of a word from -*y* to -*ies* when forming
the plural), and common homophones (e.g., *hair-hare*).

© Macmillan/McGraw-Hill

Name _____

- Every **sentence** has a subject.
- The **subject** of a sentence tells what or whom the sentence is about.

Add a subject to each group of words.

1. _____ hopped into the water.

2. _____ was bright and warm.

3. _____ buzzed near the flowers.

4. _____ is orange and black.

5. _____ perched on the branches.

6. _____ drifted across the sky.

7. _____ kept us cool.

8. _____ grew on the trees.

LC 1.2 Identify subjects and verbs that are in agreement and identify
and use pronouns, adjectives, compound words, and articles correctly in
writing and speaking.
LC 1.4 Identify and use subjects and verbs correctly in speaking and
writing simple sentences.

Name _____

> • The **subject** of a sentence tells what or whom the sentence is about.

Read the paragraph about habitat below.

My habitat each day is Lowell Elementary School. Students make up the largest group of living things in this habitat. They come in all shapes and sizes. Be very loud. They can be very quiet. Move around. Some get their food from brown lunch bags. Others get food from plastic containers. Other living things include the plants sitting near the window. Are watered every day. The living things also include the fish in the fish tank. We can watch the fish and see how they live in their habitat. Swim around in the tank.

Rewrite the paragraph, fixing any sentence fragments you found.

_____

_____

_____

_____

_____

_____

_____

_____

_____

_____

© Macmillan/McGraw-Hill

CA **LC 1.2** Identify subjects and verbs that are in agreement and identify and use pronouns, adjectives, compound words, and articles correctly in writing and speaking.
LC 1.4 Identify and use subjects and verbs correctly in speaking and writing simple sentences.

Name _____

Writing Rubric

4 Excellent	3 Good	2 Fair	1 Unsatisfactory
Ideas and Content/ Genre	Ideas and Content/ Genre	Ideas and Content/ Genre	Ideas and Content/ Genre
Organization and Focus	Organization and Focus	Organization and Focus	Organization and Focus
Sentence Structure/ Fluency	Sentence Structure/ Fluency	Sentence Structure/ Fluency	Sentence Structure/ Fluency
Conventions	Conventions	Conventions	Conventions
Word Choice	Word Choice	Word Choice	Word Choice
Voice	Voice	Voice	Voice
Presentation	Presentation	Presentation	Presentation

Name _____

Here are several spelling patterns that stand for the long *o* sound:

The letters **oa** stand for the long *o* sound. (coat)
The letters **ow** stand for the long *o* sound. (row)
When the letter **o** comes before the letters **ld**, the letter stands for the long *o* sound.

A. Fill in the missing letter or letters so that the following words have the long *o* sound. Check the rules above if you have questions.

1. s ___ ___ k

2. s n ___ ___

3. b l ___ ___

4. c ___ ___ s t

5. g ___ l d

6. l ___ ___ f

7. s c ___ l d

8. r ___ ___ s t

9. k n ___ ___

10. f l ___ ___ t

11. m ___ ___ t

12. s h ___ ___

13. b ___ ___ s t

14. f l ___ ___

15. l ___ ___ n

16. g r ___ ___

B. Follow the directions above to review these words with the long *a* sound.

17. g r ___ ___

18. p l ___ ___ n

19. s t r ___ ___ g h t

20. d e l ___ ___

© Macmillan/McGraw-Hill

CA **R 1.1** Know and use complex word families when reading (e.g., *-ight*) to decode unfamiliar words.

Name _____

A. Write the correct word from the word box on each line.

passion	splendid	ached
bothering	admire	concentrate

1. The exciting games made the party the most _____ ever!

2. I _____ the paintings of a good artist.

3. The wolf's paw _____ after he stepped on a sharp rock.

4. A person who has a strong feeling has _____.

5. The buzzing bee kept _____ me when I picked the flowers.

6. I had to _____ while I read a hard part of the story.

B. Use the words from the box to answer the questions.

7. Which word from the box has one syllable? _____

8. Write the words from the box that are two-syllable words.

   _____ _____ _____

9. Write the words from the box that are three-syllable words.

   _____ _____

Name _____

When you **compare** characters, settings, or events, you tell how they are alike.

When you **contrast** characters, settings, or events, you tell how they are different.

Read the following paragraph, and answer the questions below.

Sally and Mike are students in Mrs. Stine's classroom. They both like to read. On Friday they both went to the library to choose a book for a report. Sally chose a sports book about basketball. Mike chose a sports book about baseball. Sally wrote a long report. Mike's report was short. Mike went back to the library to check out two extra books about baseball.

1. How are Sally and Mike alike?

_____

_____

_____

_____

2. How are Sally and Mike different?

_____

_____

_____

_____

CA **R 3.3** Determine what characters are like by what they say or do and by how the author or illustrator portrays them.

Name _____

As you read *Wolf!*, fill in the Compare and Contrast Chart.

Alike	Different

How does the information you wrote in the Compare and Contrast
Chart help you generate questions about *Wolf!*?

© Macmillan/McGraw-Hill

As I read, I will pay attention to my expression.

	"You haven't eaten any lunch, Katie," my grandmother
8	said. She was right. The pile of mashed potatoes was a
19	round ball. My broccoli pieces still looked like perfect
28	little trees. And I had eaten only a spoonful of bean chili.
40	The next day, Granny was leaving on a trip to Europe.
51	She was staying on a sheep farm in Ireland for a month.
63	Traveling the world was Granny's passion, but I was
72	worried.
73	"With all those sheep, there might be wolves," I told
83	her. "It could be dangerous."
88	"You've been reading too many fairy tales," Granny
96	said.
97	I had read plenty of fairy tales. But I had also read a lot
111	of nonfiction. 113

Comprehension Check

1. Why is Katie worried? **Plot**

2. What does Granny think of Katie's fear about the wolves? **Make Inferences**

	Words Read	–	Number of Errors	=	Words Correct Score
First Read		–		=	
Second Read		–		=	

CA **R 1.3** Read aloud narrative and expository text fluently and accurately and with appropriate pacing, intonation, and expression.

> **Boldface type, headings, italics,** and **pronunciation** can help you better understand important information in the text.

Look at the numbered parts of the article. Identify each text feature from the list below. Write the correct feature on each line.

boldface type

heading

italics

pronunciation key

---

(1) Animals in the Wild

Animals living in the wild know they must take care of themselves. Animals know this because they were born with (2)**instinct** (3)(in´ • stingkt´) and don't have to learn how to do things. For example, wolves know to make their home in a place called a (4)*den*. They know that the den must be well hidden to keep the young wolves safe.

---

1. _____

2. _____

3. _____

4. _____

5. Based on the information in the article, what is the definition of *instinct*?

_____

_____

CA **R 2.1** Use titles, tables of contents, chapter headings, glossaries, and indexes to locate information in text.

Name _____

Suppose you find a word you don't understand as you are reading. You look up the word in the dictionary and find it has more than one meaning. How do you know which meaning is correct?

- Read the definitions.
- Try each meaning in the sentence to see if it makes sense.

Read the dictionary entry. Then write the letter of the correct meaning on the line next to each sentence below.

> **load** *noun* 1. something carried: *There is a load of hay in the wagon.*
> 2. the amount that can be carried: *One load of stones will fill in the ditch.*
> 3. something that weighs on the mind: *Leaving the dentist's office took a load off my mind.*
> *verb* 4. to put a load in or on something: *Let's load the hay into the wagon.*
> 5. to put something into a device: *Do you know how to load film into that camera?*

a. Finishing his book report took a load off Justin's mind. _____

b. Ms. Gomez will show us how to load that program into the computer.

_____

c. Will one load of bricks be enough to build the wall? _____

d. The truck carried a load of fresh fruit to the market. _____

e. Tomorrow morning we will load the car and start our trip. _____

© Macmillan/McGraw-Hill

CA R 1.0 Word Analysis, Fluency, and Systematic Vocabulary Development

Name _____

Using the Word Study Steps

1. LOOK at the word.

2. SAY the word aloud.

3. STUDY the letters in the word.

4. WRITE the word.

5. CHECK the word.
   Did you spell the word right?
   If not, go back to step 1.

A. Fill in the missing letters to create a spelling word.

1. s h _____ _____   9. s _____ l d

2. r _____ _____ s t   10. b _____ _____ l

3. s c _____ l d   11. c _____ _____ l

4. b l _____ _____   12. s l _____ _____

5. f l _____ _____ t   13. l _____ _____ f

6. g _____ l d   14. s n _____ _____

7. g r _____ _____ s   15. s _____ _____ k

8. c _____ _____ s t

B. Choose the spelling word that best completes the sentence.

1. The boat will _____ on the lake.

2. _____ fell all night and covered the ground.

3. I like to have a _____ of ice cream for dessert.

© Macmillan/McGraw-Hill

LC 1.8 Spell correctly one-syllable words that have blends, contractions, compounds, orthographic patterns (e.g., *qu*, consonant doubling, changing the ending of a word from -*y* to -*ies* when forming the plural), and common homophones (e.g., *hair-hare*).

Wolf! • **Grade 3/Unit I** **53**

Name _____

A. There are seven spelling mistakes in this postcard. Circle the misspelled words. Write the words correctly on the lines below.

Dear Paula,

I told you I would send you a postcard! You sure do need to come here next summer. We had so much fun on our family vacation. We would sit on beaches that had sand the color of solid golde. The other penguins and I would play on the beach, flowte in the water, and soke up the sun. At night we would stay up late to listen to the singing of the whales while eating a big boal of ice cream.

I am sad that we have to leave the coste in a few days and go home to Antarctica. I hope there isn't too much sno at home. I will shoe you pictures when I get home.

      See you soon,
      Peter

1. _____   5. _____

2. _____   6. _____

3. _____   7. _____

4. _____

Writing Activity

B. Write about what you like to do on a cold or snowy day. Use at least three spelling words in your description.

_____

_____

_____

_____

_____

© Macmillan/McGraw-Hill

LC 1.8 Spell correctly one-syllable words that have blends, contractions, compounds, orthographic patterns (e.g., *qu*, consonant doubling, changing the ending of a word from -*y* to -*ies* when forming the plural), and common homophones (e.g., *hair-hare*).

Name _____

> • Every sentence has two parts.
> • Every sentence has a **predicate**.
> • The **predicate** of a sentence tells what the subject does or is.

Match each group of words in the first column with its predicate in the second column. Write the predicate.

1. Ice and snow

_____

2. The ice

_____

3. Temperatures

_____

4. Cold wind

_____

5. Giant icebergs

_____

6. Seals and penguins

_____

7. Few plants

_____

8. Tourists

_____

stay below freezing.
float in the sea.
like to see Antarctica.
grow in Antarctica.
cover Antarctica.
blows across the land.
live in the cold.
is millions of years old.

LC 1.4 Identify and use subjects and verbs correctly in speaking and writing simple sentences.

• The **predicate** of a sentence tells what the subject does or is.

Rewrite the paragraphs below. Be sure to correct each run-on sentence.

My mom loves to visit Antarctica. She goes there every winter she wants me to go with her one day. She travels there for work she is an animal doctor who works with penguins. My mom helps sick penguins feel better she also works with the local animal doctors to help find cures for diseases

One time, my mom got stuck in Antarctica. She could not fly home for a week. I was worried about her, but she called me every day to tell me that she was okay. Maybe I will go to Antarctica one day with my mom I just do not want to get stuck

_____

_____

_____

_____

_____

_____

_____

_____

_____

_____

LC 1.4 Identify and use subjects and verbs correctly in speaking and writing simple sentences.

Name _____

1. Look carefully at one of your arms.

2. Write 4 sentences <u>only</u> about your arm. Focus on the object and describe exactly how it looks.

Example: My right arm looks pale sticking out of my dark blue t-shirt. Freckles make it look like the map of constellations that hangs in our classroom. If I look hard enough, I think I can make out Orion's belt near my wrist. It's right next to the jagged, white scar that my cat, George, gave me when I tried to put him in a doll's dress last year.

_____

_____

_____

_____

_____

_____

_____

_____

Extra Practice: Do the same exercise, describing one of your feet.

Name _____

Remember the following common spellings for the long *i* sound:
i, *ie*, *y*, and *igh*.

**A. Find the two words in each sentence that have the long *i*
sound, and write them on the lines provided.**

1. Why is the sky so blue? _____ _____

2. The child got into a fight. _____ _____

3. Dad went to buy a tie at the store. _____

   _____

4. I might ask the cook to fry the food. _____

   _____

5. Can you find a bright red paint for the barn? _____

   _____

**B. Write the word in each sentence that has the long *i* sound.
Underline the letter or letters that stand for the sound.**

6. Did you know that pilot fish swim near blue sharks? _____

7. A bear once walked in front of my dad's car. _____

8. We need to pry open this box. _____

9. The lights went out during the storm. _____

10. What is your favorite pie? _____

11. The pesky fly almost ruined our picnic. _____

12. Sam eats only mild food. _____

(CA) **R 1.1** Know and use complex word families when reading
(e.g., *-ight*) to decode unfamiliar words.

Name _____

| determination | ruined | storage |
| exact | separate | luckiest |

A. Fill in the blank with the word from the box that best completes each sentence.

1. Rose's family had planned their trip with great _____.

2. The family's furniture was put into a room for _____ on the ship.

3. The ship sailed at the _____ time it was supposed to leave.

4. Rose used a sheet to _____ her space from the rest of her family.

5. She thought she was the _____ person on the ship. She had her own quiet space to write in her journal.

6. Rose unpacked at her new home. Some boxes had been squashed. Nothing had been broken or _____ during the move.

B. Write a sentence using one of the vocabulary words.

7. _____

   _____

When you make a **prediction**, you tell what you think will probably happen next. As you continue reading, you can **confirm** your prediction, or find out if you were right.

Each poem tells about characters who spend time in a place of their own. Read each poem. Read the title of the poem to help you predict what will happen. Choose the words that tell what will probably happen next and write the words on the line.

1.   **Finally We Can Play**

Rain has fallen for days and days.

We've been bored in many ways.

The sun is finally out today.

We can't wait _____.

a. for the sky to turn gray.

b. to run out and play.

2.   **The Tired Queen**

The queen went to sleep late last night.

She stayed up 'til almost dawn.

When she wakes up later this morning,

You'll _____.

a. find her mowing her lawn.

b. probably see her yawn.

CA **R 3.2** Comprehend basic plots of classic fairy tales, myths, folktales, legends, and fables from around the world.

Name _____

As you read *My Very Own Room*, fill in the Predictions Chart.

What I Predict	What Happens

How does the information you wrote in this Predictions Chart help you understand plot development in *My Very Own Room*?

 R 3.2 Comprehend basic plots of classic fairy tales, myths, folktales, legends, and fables from around the world.

© Macmillan/McGraw-Hill

As I read, I will pay attention to phrasing.

10	"What are your plans for today?" Mr. Sanchez asked his son Carlo.
12	"I'm hiking with my nature club," Carlo said, "from
21	the state park entrance to Turtle Lake. Jimmy's father,
30	Mr. Gordon, is going with us."
36	"It's colder than yesterday," his mother said. "Please
44	take your warmest jacket and your gloves."
51	"Hold on," Carlo's father said. "I need to get your warm
62	blue jacket from the storage box in the attic. Then I'll
73	drop you off."
76	A short time later, Carlo met up with Mr. Gordon and
87	the other members of the club, Jimmy, Julie, and Tyrone.
97	Mr. Gordon packed them in his van and drove them to
108	the state park.
111	When they arrived he checked his compass. "The
119	old logging trail is somewhere directly west of here,"
128	he said. 130

Comprehension Check

1. What are Carlo's plans? **Main Idea and Details**

2. What is the weather like? **Plot Development**

	Words Read	−	Number of Errors	=	Words Correct Score
First Read		−		=	
Second Read		−		=	

© Macmillan/McGraw-Hill

CA **R 1.3** Read aloud narrative and expository text fluently and accurately and with appropriate pacing, intonation, and expression.

An encyclopedia is a set of books filled with articles. The articles are in alphabetical order and give information about many subjects. On the top of each page is a **guide word** that tells the reader what will be on that page. Some articles have **headings** and subheadings in boldface type to summarize information and make it easy to find. Sometimes there are pictures with **captions,** which explain the pictures.

210   **Painters**

Vincent van Gogh's Life
Vincent van Gogh was born ▬▬▬▬
▬▬▬▬▬▬▬▬▬▬▬▬▬
▬▬▬▬▬▬▬▬▬▬▬▬▬
Early paintings Van Gogh's early
paintings were ▬▬▬▬▬▬

Vincent van Gogh
painted beautiful
pictures.

Answer the following questions about the encyclopedia article above.

1. What page is it on? _____

2. What is the guide word? _____

3. What is the heading? _____

4. What is the subheading? _____

5. What is the caption? _____

_____

R 2.1 Use titles, tables of contents, chapter headings, glossaries, and
indexes to locate information in text.

> The **inflectional endings -*er*** and **-*est*** show comparison. The
> ending **-*er*** means "more." The ending **-*est*** means "most."

**A. Write the correct form of the adjective shown below each
blank line. Use -*er* or -*est* to compare the items.**

1. The giraffe was the _____ of all the giraffes in the zoo.
   tall

2. She had the _____ neck of all of the animals in the zoo.
   long

3. She was even _____ than her brother.
   big

4. She thought that the leaves at the very tops of the trees were the

   _____.
   sweet

5. She shared the _____ of the three spaces in their home
   large

   with two other giraffes.

6. The breezes were _____ at night than in the day.
   cool

7. When the giraffe grew a little _____, she got a big surprise.
   old

   She got her own space!

B. Add -*er* or -*est* to the word *great* and use it in a sentence.

8. _____

   _____

CA R 1.0 Word Analysis, Fluency, and Systematic Vocabulary Development

bright	fry
buy	might
child	mild
dye	pie
fight	right
flight	tied
find	tight

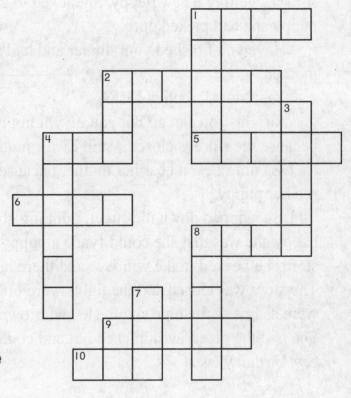

Crossword Puzzle

Read the clues. Then use the spelling words to complete the sentences.

ACROSS

1. The flavor is very_____.

2. The plane _____ was long.

4. I ___ milk for my new kitten.

5. The pants were too _____.

6. David _____ his shoes.

8. I cannot _____ my winter coat.

9. My answer was _____.

10. She uses ____ to color her hair.

DOWN

1. He closed the door with all his _____.

2. Let's _____ fish for dinner.

3. The _____ missed his mother.

4. The sun is very _____.

7. We ate apple _____.

8. The two angry dogs got into a _____.

LC 1.8 Spell correctly one-syllable words that have blends, contractions, compounds, orthographic patterns (e.g., *qu*, consonant doubling, changing the ending of a word from *-y* to *-ies* when forming the plural), and common homophones (e.g., *hair-hare*).

Name _____

A. There are seven spelling mistakes in these paragraphs. Circle the misspelled words. Write the words correctly on the lines below.

"Mom, can I leave yet?" yelled Lisa. Tomorrow was Lisa's birthday and she was getting a new puppy. She loved to go to the pet store and look at the puppy she had picked out.

"Have you finished your dinner and had a piece of pye?" asked Lisa's mother.

"Yes, Mom," replied Lisa.

"Alright, you can go but you myght not be able to see your puppy because the store is closed," said Lisa's mother.

Lisa didn't even hear her mother because she ran rieght out the door to see her puppy.

Lisa skipped down the street, thinking about her new puppy and how happy she was that she could fynde a puppy she liked. When she got to the store she peeked in the window, and there he was playing in his wire cage. The store was closed and the lights were off but she could see his eyes that were as brit as the blue skigh. He had brown fur and his tail was all black. She had the green leash picked out and couldn't wait to bie it. This was the best birthday ever!

1. _____   4. _____   7. _____

2. _____   5. _____

3. _____   6. _____

Writing Activity

B. Write about something you can't wait to happen. Use at least three spelling words in your description.

_____

_____

_____

LC 1.8 Spell correctly one-syllable words that have blends, contractions, compounds, orthographic patterns (e.g., *qu*, consonant doubling, changing the ending of a word from *-y* to *-ies* when forming the plural), and common homophones (e.g., *hair-hare*).

© Macmillan/McGraw-Hill

Name _____

> • A sentence that contains two sentences joined by **and** is called a **compound sentence**.

Write a compound sentence by joining each pair of sentences. Use a comma and the word *and*.

1. Hamsters are fun. They are easy to care for.

_____

_____

2. Hamsters are small. They are quiet.

_____

_____

3. Some hamsters have long hair. Some have short hair.

_____

_____

4. Hamsters are small. They can fit in your pocket.

_____

_____

5. They stuff food in their cheeks. They carry it that way.

_____

_____

LC 1.6 Use commas in dates, locations, and addresses and for items in a series.

Name _____

- A sentence that contains two sentences joined by *and* is called a **compound sentence**.
- Use a comma before *and* when you join two sentences to form a compound sentence.

Read the paragraph, and look for sentences you can combine. Then rewrite the paragraph.

   I observed my cat, Eddie. Then I studied my dog, Belle. Eddie is orange. He weighs twenty pounds. Belle is white. She weighs twelve pounds. Both like to sleep. Both like to be in the sun. Eddie likes to chase birds. He likes to climb. Belle likes to dig. She plays fetch. Eddie sleeps on my bed. Belle sleeps on my floor. They are both good. They make great pets.

_____

_____

_____

_____

_____

_____

_____

(CA) **LC 1.6** Use commas in dates, locations, and addresses and for items in a series.

1. Read the following sentence:

The room was a mess.

2. Imagine a messy room that you have seen.

3. Write 2–4 sentences describing one moment in that messy room.

Example: My brother's room was so messy that I couldn't see the floor. I felt like I was wading through an ocean of dirty laundry as I walked over to his desk to get the book I wanted to borrow. There was a moldy, half-eaten sandwich next to his computer and all I could smell were his stinky socks.

_____

_____

_____

_____

_____

_____

_____

_____

Extra Practice: Do the same exercise describing a different type of room.

Name _____

Say the following words that have the **long e** sound. Notice there are three different spellings for the **long** *e* sound:

e–m**e**   **ee**–f**ee**t   **ea**–h**ea**t

A. Fill in the missing letters e, ee, or ea to form a word that makes sense in the blank in each sentence.

1. I asked my sister to come to the play, but sh_____ did not want to come.

2. Let's s_____l the letter and mail it.

3. That movie is about a m_____n man named Scrooge.

4. Many performers f_____l nervous before going on stage.

5. The conductor lost the sh_____t music for the song.

B. Write a sentence for each of the following words with the long e sound.

6. freeze _____

_____

7. free _____

_____

8. bean _____

_____

CA   **R 1.1** Know and use complex word families when reading (e.g., *-ight*) to decode unfamiliar words.

Name _____

| lonesome   wailed   traders   blossomed   sidewalks   grumbled |

A. Use a word from the box to answer each question. Use each word only once.

1. How might you feel if you moved to a new town where you did not know

   anyone? _____

2. What is another word for *complained in a low voice*?

   _____

3. What is the safest place for people to walk? _____

4. What word might describe an idea that grew very quickly?

   _____

5. Who might be upset if they couldn't sell their goods?

   _____

6. What did the coyote do when it lifted its head toward the moon?

   _____

B. Write a sentence using each of the vocabulary words below.

7. lonesome _____

   _____

8. grumbled _____

   _____

In a story, the events happen in chronological order or **sequence**.

Read the events below, which are out of order. Then write the events in the order that they happened.

a. Many people liked the shirt that Jessica sewed for her brother.

b. As the business grew, Jessica could not keep up with all the work.

c. Soon Jessica started a children's clothing business.

d. Jessica and her family moved to California to seek gold.

e. Jessica cut up an old sheet to make a shirt for her brother.

f. When Jessica convinced her brother and two friends to help, her business blossomed.

1. _____

_____

2. _____

_____

3. _____

_____

4. _____

_____

5. _____

_____

6. _____

_____

© Macmillan/McGraw-Hill

Name _____

As you read *Boom Town*, fill in the Sequence Chart.

Sequence Chart

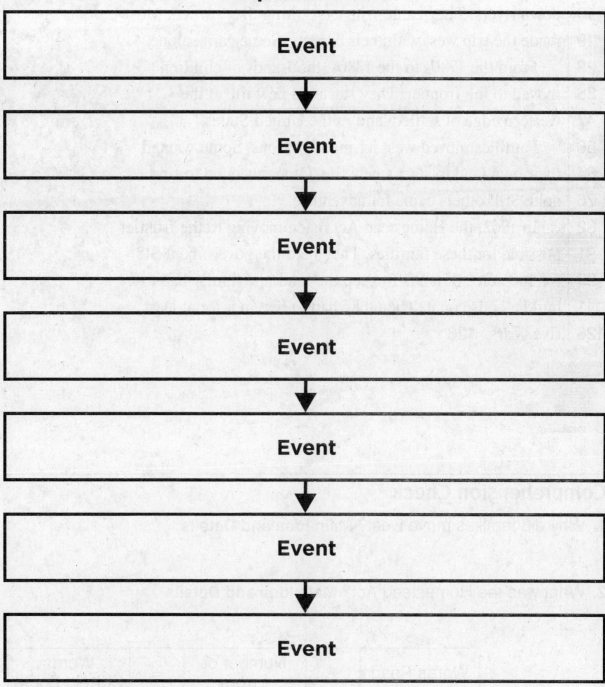

Event

Event

Event

Event

Event

Event

Event

How does the information you wrote in this Sequence Chart help you understand chronological order in *Boom Town*?

As I read, I will pay attention to punctuation.

	They came by horse and wagon. They came by flatboat
10	down rivers. They came with everything they owned. Most
19	made the trip west with their parents. Some came alone.
29	From the 1780s to the 1880s, thousands of children
36	moved to the frontier. They started a new life at the
47	western edge of settled land in the United States.
56	Families moved west for many reasons. Some wanted
64	their own land to start a new life. Others wanted to find
76	gold. Still others came for adventure.
82	In 1862, the Homestead Act made moving to the frontier
91	possible for these families. They paid the government $18
99	for 160 acres of land. To keep the land, the family had to
111	build a house on it. Then they had to live in it for at least
126	five years. 128

Comprehension Check

1. Why did families move west? **Main Idea and Details**

2. What was the Homestead Act? **Main Idea and Details**

	Words Read	–	Number of Errors	=	Words Correct Score
First Read		–		=	
Second Read		–		=	

CA **R 1.3** Read aloud narrative and expository text fluently and accurately and with appropriate pacing, intonation, and expression.

Name _____

A **calendar** helps you organize and keep track of important dates.

Use the information below to fill in the calendar. Enter the words in boldface type on the calendar.

July

Sunday	Monday	Tuesday	Wednesday	Thursday	Friday	Saturday
						1
2	3	4	5	6	7	8
9	10	11	12	13	14	15
16	17	18	19	20	21	22
23	24	25	26	27	28	29
30	31					

1. July 6 and 7: Buy **ingredients** for lemonade stand.

2. July 8: **Make posters** and signs to advertise lemonade stand.

3. July 9: **Put up posters** in town.

4. July 10, 11, 12, and 13: **Sell** lemonade at corner of Main and First Streets.

5. July 14: Count money earned and take it to **bank**.

6. July 17: Leave for family **vacation**.

© Macmillan/McGraw-Hill

CA **R 2.1** Use titles, tables of contents, chapter headings, glossaries, and indexes to locate information in text.

Sometimes you can figure out the meaning of a **compound word** from the meanings of the two smaller words. Other times, you need to look up the words in a dictionary to find the meaning.

Underline the compound word in each sentence. Then write its definition. Use a dictionary to help you.

1. Anna and her family traveled by stagecoach to California.

   _____

   _____

2. Anna spent her daytime hours sewing clothing.

   _____

   _____

3. Anna would use a landmark so she would not get lost while walking to

   the store. _____

   _____

4. The blacksmith in town traded some tools for a new shirt.

   _____

   _____

5. One day a cowboy rode into town and asked Anna to sew him a new

   shirt. _____

   _____

© Macmillan/McGraw-Hill

CA **R 1.0** Word Analysis, Fluency, and Systematic Vocabulary Development

bean	field	seal
clean	freeze	street
cream	green	team
creek	heel	weak

Crossword Puzzle

Solve the crossword puzzle with spelling words that complete the sentences.

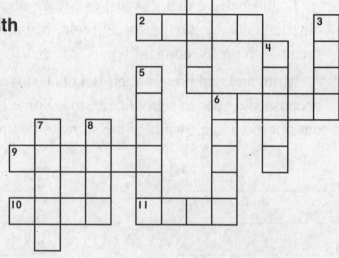

ACROSS

2. After the show, we _____ the dressing rooms.

6. There is a scene in the play that happens near a watery _____.

9. If you leave the water outside, it will _____.

10. James played the part of a baby _____ in the zoo scene.

11. I clap when my _____ scores a goal.

DOWN

1. The ants carried a small black _____ away from the picnic.

3. I was too _____ to carry the heavy sets.

4. We passed a _____ that was lit by a beautiful sunset.

5. Sometimes we play our guitars on the _____ to make extra money.

6. Aunt Sarah likes to put _____ in her tea.

7. I painted the leaves on the forest set bright _____.

8. Some gum got stuck under the _____ of my shoe.

LC 1.8 Spell correctly one-syllable words that have blends, contractions, compounds, orthographic patterns (e.g., *qu*, consonant doubling, changing the ending of a word from -y to -ies when forming the plural), and common homophones (e.g., *hair-hare*).

Name _____

A. Proofreading

There are six spelling mistakes in these paragraphs. Circle the misspelled words. Write the words correctly on the lines below.

This year I joined the dance teem at school. It's been so much fun. We've been practicing for a long time for our big show. I play the part of a butterfly. I get to do one dance all by myself.

I can't believe that it is just one weke away. The teachers helped us build our stage outside on the soccer feeld. My mom made my costume. It's dark grean with pretty, colorful wings. Mom also fixed the loose heal of my shoe.

Mom and dad bought their tickets last week. My sister gets hers for frie because she goes to school here, too. Some of the other dancers are nervous, but not me. I can't wait for the show to begin.

1. _____   4. _____

2. _____   5. _____

3. _____   6. _____

B. Writing Activity

Describe a favorite after-school activity. Use at least four spelling words in your description.

_____

_____

_____

_____

_____

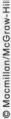

LC 1.8 Spell correctly one-syllable words that have blends, contractions, compounds, orthographic patterns (e.g., *qu*, consonant doubling, changing the ending of a word from -y to -ies when forming the plural), and common homophones (e.g., *hair-hare*).

Name _____

• The name of a day, month, or holiday begins with a capital letter.

Complete each sentence by writing the name of the day, month, or holiday correctly.

1. We found an anthill on saturday. _____

2. We looked for it again on sunday. _____

3. It kept getting bigger during june. _____

4. More and more ants came during july. _____

5. The busy ants worked hard in august. _____

6. There was less action on labor day. _____

7. The ant hill was quiet by halloween. _____

8. It was gone on thanksgiving day. _____

9. Father is off on monday. _____

10. Next month is mother's day. _____

11. I like spring weather in may. _____

12. We ate pancakes on new year's day. _____

13. We saw fireworks on independence day. _____

14. Squirrels gathered acorns in november. _____

15. It can be very cold in january. _____

16. Next week is valentine's day. _____

© Macmillan/McGraw-Hill

LC 1.7 Capitalize geographical names, holidays, historical periods, and special events correctly.

Name _____

- Begin a proper noun with a capital letter.
- Begin the name of a day, month, or holiday with a capital letter.

A. Look at the underlined nouns. Put a C over common nouns. Put a P over proper nouns.

The students in <u>ms. harris's</u> class would like an ant farm. An ant

farm is a good way to learn <u>science</u>. It lets students practice their

observation skills. It shows us how <u>insects</u> live and work. It takes less

care than <u>fish</u> or a guinea pig.

Ant farms are sold at <u>tom's toy shop</u>. The students would like to get one

before <u>thanksgiving</u>.

B. Writing Activity

Rewrite the paragraphs so that proper nouns begin with capital letters and common nouns begin with lowercase letters.

_____

_____

_____

_____

_____

_____

CA **LC 1.7** Capitalize geographical names, holidays, historical periods, and special events correctly.

© Macmillan/McGraw-Hill

Name _____

1. Please read the following sentence:

    Something was wrong with the car.

2. Write three things that could be wrong with how the car looks.

    _____

    _____

    _____

3. Write three things that could be wrong with how the car sounds.

    _____

    _____

    _____

4. Write three things that could be wrong with the way the car moves.

    _____

    _____

    _____

5. Using these ideas, now write two more sentences that tell what is wrong with the car.

Example: We heard a loud, annoying clacking coming from the back of the car and smoke was coming out from under the hood. My mom tried to make a right turn, but the car would only turn left.

    _____

    _____

    _____

Extra Practice: Use this sentence and follow the same directions:

    Something was wrong with my friend.

CA **W 1.0** Writing Strategies

Some words have **silent consonants**. They are usually part of a pair of consonants. The first consonant in the consonant patterns **wr, kn,** and **gn** is silent.

For example: **wrong, knife,** and **gnaw** all have silent consonants at the beginning of the word.

Write the two consonants that complete the word in each sentence below. Then write the sound they stand for.

| gn | kn | wr |

1. The author likes to ___ ___ i t e her stories as she listens to music. ___

2. I ___ ___ o w how to play the violin. ___

3. The s i ___ ___ was printed in three languages. ___

4. The author's first book was about a ___ ___ i g h t who rescued a princess from the tower. ___

5. We each ___ ___ o t e letters to the author telling her how much we liked the story. ___

6. The ___ ___ a t was buzzing around my face. ___

7. We had to tie a ___ ___ o t in the rope so the boat wouldn't drift away. ___

8. I had to ___ ___ a p the book I was giving my friend so he wouldn't know what it was. ___

CA   **R 1.1** Know and use complex word families when reading (e.g., *-ight*) to decode unfamiliar words.

Name _____

Read each clue. Then fill in the crossword puzzle with the correct word from the box.

disappear	protect	harming
supply	capture	enclosure

Across

1. causing injury

4. to catch or get hold of

5. to go away completely

Down

2. to keep from harm

3. a structure that keeps things closed in

6. an amount available for use

A conclusion is what you decide after you have thought about something. You can use your own experience and relevant details to help you **draw conclusions** in a story.

Draw your conclusions about the story below by answering each question.

At a recent neighborhood meeting, people talked about planting a vegetable garden. There was a vacant lot nearby, but it was filled with garbage. Ivan raised his hand and said, "I have a great idea, but it will take a lot of work." That was it! The next Saturday, we all got to work.

Ivan took charge. He asked people what they wanted to do. Then he helped them get started. Some people cleared garbage from the vacant lot. Other people loaded garbage bags onto a truck. Everyone worked hard.

We were all tired at the end of the day, but the lot looked great. Now we were ready for the next step.

1. From the information in the passage, what makes you think Ivan is a good leader?

   _____

   _____

   _____

2. What do you think will happen next? What leads you to this conclusion?

   _____

   _____

   _____

© Macmillan/McGraw-Hill

CA **R 2.6** Extract appropriate and significant information from the text, including problems and solutions.

Name _____

As you read *Home-Grown Butterflies*, fill in the Conclusion Map.

```
┌─────────────────────────────────────┐
│                Clue                  │
│                                      │
│                                      │
└─────────────────────────────────────┘
                  ↓
┌─────────────────────────────────────┐
│                Clue                  │
│                                      │
│                                      │
└─────────────────────────────────────┘
                  ↓
┌─────────────────────────────────────┐
│                Clue                  │
│                                      │
│                                      │
└─────────────────────────────────────┘
                  ↓
┌─────────────────────────────────────┐
│             Conclusion               │
│                                      │
│                                      │
│                                      │
└─────────────────────────────────────┘
```

How does the information you wrote in this Conclusion Map help you understand relevant details in *Home-Grown Butterflies*?

R 2.6 Extract appropriate and significant information from the text, including problems and solutions.

© Macmillan/McGraw-Hill

Name _____

As I read, I will pay attention to pacing.

	Purple loosestrife has been around a long time. It is a
11	native plant in Europe and Asia. The plant did not become
22	a pest in those places. It didn't grow out of control as it has
36	here. In fact, some people thought it was a helpful herb.
47	They used it as a medicine. How did it get from there to
60	here?
61	Purple loosestrife came to North America in the 1800s,
69	but no one is sure how it traveled. Could seeds have been
81	carried across the sea in ships?
87	Many people believe a supply of seeds arrived in the
97	baggage of new immigrants. They planted the seeds in
106	their new gardens. The purple flowers may have reminded
115	them of home.
118	Purple loosestrife did not grow out of control in Europe
128	and Asia. It did not kill its plant neighbors. Why? The
139	answer is simple. Purple loosestrife had natural enemies
147	in its homeland. 150

Comprehension Check

1. How was purple loosestrife controlled in Asia and Europe? **Problem and Solution**

2. What might be a good way to control loosestrife in America? **Plot Development**

	Words Read	–	Number of Errors	=	Words Correct Score
First Read		–		=	
Second Read		–		=	

© Macmillan/McGraw-Hill

CA R 1.3 Read aloud narrative and expository text fluently and accurately and with appropriate pacing, intonation, and expression.

Name _____

Personification and **assonance** are literary devices that poets use to create pleasing images and sounds. Personification gives human characteristics to animals or things. Assonance is the repetition of the same or similar middle vowel sound in a series of words grouped closely together.

Read the poem. Then answer the questions.

One day a girl went walking
And stepped into a store;
She bought a pound of sausages
And laid them on the floor.

The girl began to whistle
A merry little tune;
Soon the sausages jumped up
And danced around the room.

1. Find the two words that create assonance in the first set of lines. Write

   the words on the line. _____

2. Find the three words that create assonance in the second set of lines.

   Write the words on the line. _____

3. In the poem, what things talk or act the way a person might?

   _____

4. What do they do or say in the poem? _____

   _____

© Macmillan/McGraw-Hill

Name _____

Practice

Vocabulary Strategy:
Multiple-Meaning
Words

In a dictionary, you may find different meanings for a word. The correct meaning depends on the way the word is used in the sentence.

Use the dictionary entry to answer each question.

duck (duk) *Noun* 1. A water bird that has a broad, flat bill and webbed feet that help it to swim. There are both wild and tame ducks. Tame ducks are often raised for food.
Verb 1. to lower the head or bend down quickly: *The batter ducked to keep from being hit by the ball.* 2. to avoid; evade: *I ducked the embarrassing question by bringing up another subject.*

1. We can fool my brother if you duck under the table as soon as you see him.

   Duck means _____.

2. We saw only one duck on the partly frozen lake.

   Duck means _____

   _____

3. She ducked out of the room through a side door to escape.

   Duck means _____.

4. Did you duck when all the butterflies flew near you?

   What part of speech is the word *duck*? _____

CA R 1.7 Use a dictionary to learn the meaning and other features of unknown words.

Name _____

Using the Word Study Steps

1. LOOK at the word.
2. SAY the word aloud.
3. STUDY the letters in the word.

4. WRITE the word.
5. CHECK the word.
   Did you spell the word right?
   If not, go back to step 1.

Find Rhyming Words

Circle the word in each row that rhymes with the word in dark type.

1. **trap**	rip	tarp	wrap
2. **float**	foam	flat	wrote
3. **song**	wrong	sing	roam
4. **sight**	style	sit	knight
5. **rock**	known	knock	roll
6. **mine**	sign	mend	mint
7. **flaws**	gnaws	flame	naps
8. **sing**	wring	sang	write
9. **bit**	bite	knit	bait
10. **deck**	dock	deal	wreck
11. **sat**	gnat	gale	still
12. **glow**	glee	know	blew
13. **mists**	mast	gusts	wrists
14. **blots**	blast	knots	cost
15. **sight**	write	seen	shell

© Macmillan/McGraw-Hill

LC 1.8 Spell correctly one-syllable words that have blends,
contractions, compounds, orthographic patterns (e.g., *qu*, consonant
doubling, changing the ending of a word from -y to -ies when forming
the plural), and common homophones (e.g., *hair-hare*).

Home-Grown Butterflies **89**
Grade 3/Unit 2

A. Proofreading

There are five spelling mistakes in this letter. Circle the misspelled words. Write the words correctly on the lines below.

Dear Diary,

An author came to school today to tell us about the book she wroat. It took her two years! It is about the many adventures of a nite. First, he is on a ship. Then, he is captured by an evil band of robbers. In the end, he becomes a king.

It is exciting to noe someone who is an author. I think I want to rit a book when I grow up. It would be about something I love. Maybe it will be about a lady who likes to nit pretty scarves and hats, just like my grandmother. Or maybe it will be about about my pet dog. Who knows!

I will write more tomorrow,

Alice

1. _____   3. _____   5. _____

2. _____   4. _____

B. Writing Activity

Write about a book you would like to write. Use at least four spelling words in your description.

_____

_____

_____

_____

CA LC 1.8 Spell correctly one-syllable words that have blends, contractions, compounds, orthographic patterns (e.g., *qu*, consonant doubling, changing the ending of a word from -y to -ies when forming the plural), and common homophones (e.g., *hair-hare*).

Name _____

• Add **-es** to form the plural of singular nouns that end in **s, sh, ch,** or **x.**
• To form the plural of nouns ending in a consonant and **y,** change the **y** to **i** and add **-es.**

A. Change each word to a plural noun.

1. worry _____   6. path _____

2. wish _____   7. flash _____

3. bench _____   8. porch _____

4. box _____   9. mix _____

5. bus _____   10. kiss _____

B. Write the plural form of each noun in parentheses.

11. There are several (library) _____.

12. The books are filled with (story) _____.

13. There are trees and (bush) _____ outside the library.

14. You can read under the (branch) _____.

15. I read a story about a wolf that lived with (fox) _____.

16. I was able to read on one of the (bench) _____.

17. Animals can hear you if you step on (stick) _____.

18. Ned found salamanders under several (rock) _____.

19. Look carefully and you'll see a variety of (grass) _____.

20. In the woods, we camped out in (tent) _____.

- Add **-s** to form the plural of most singular nouns.
- Add **-es** to form the plural of singular nouns that end in **s**, **sh**, **ch**, or **x**.
- To form the plural of nouns ending in a consonant and **y**, change the **y** to **i** and add **-es**.

A. On the lines below, write the correct plural version of the underlined nouns from the poster.

_____   _____

_____   _____

_____   _____

B. Writing Activity

Rewrite the paragraph on the poster using plural nouns. Make sure every sentence begins with a capital letter and ends with an end mark.

WILD THINGS

You can learn all kinds of wild things at <u>library</u>   you can find fun <u>story</u>   you can discover interesting <u>fact</u>   you can take out movies   And it is all free!   now get wild and go to your library   Get <u>box</u> of <u>book</u>, and learn <u>bunch</u> of things

_____

_____

_____

_____

CA **LC 1.0** Written and Oral English Language Conventions

Name _____

1. Read the following sentence:

  She was afraid.

2. Write a sentence about what she might be doing.

  _____

3. Write a sentence about a sound she might make.

  _____

4. Describe her face.

  _____

  _____

5. Now using these details, write 3 more sentences that show the girl was afraid.

Example: The girl cowered behind the chair, frozen. She could hardly breathe. Her legs began to shake as the sound of footsteps in the hallway got closer and closer.

  _____

  _____

  _____

  _____

  _____

  _____

Extra Practice: Do the same activity using the following sentence:

  The man was angry.

Name _____

Some words begin with the letters *str*, *scr*, *spr*, or *thr*. Say each of these words: **stream, scrap, spread, throw**.

Fill in the missing letters *str*, *scr*, *spr*, or *thr* to complete each word. Then use the word in a sentence.

1. _____ + ong = _____

Sentence: _____

_____

2. _____ + ow = _____

Sentence: _____

_____

3. _____ + ape = _____

Sentence: _____

_____

4. _____ + out = _____

Sentence: _____

_____

5. _____ + one = _____

Sentence: _____

_____

CA **R 1.1** Know and use complex word families when reading (e.g., *-ight*) to decode unfamiliar words.

Name _____

A. Fill in each blank with the correct word from the box.

| culture   communities   immigrants   established   traditional |

    In California, there are many different types of _____,

or neighborhoods. These neighborhoods were _____ by

newcomers who moved to California from regions around the world. These

_____ wanted new lives in America. To keep from feeling

homesick, the newcomers tried to do things in _____ ways.

They brought their _____ and traditions with them. These new

neighborhoods make California interesting and unique.

B. Using the clues in the story, write the definitions of these vocabulary words. Check your definitions with a dictionary.

1. communities _____

_____

2. immigrants _____

_____

3. established _____

4. culture _____

5. traditional _____

_____

Name _____

The **main idea** of a paragraph or section is what it is mostly about. The main idea is often stated.

Supporting **details** are ideas or facts that give more information about the main idea. Most of the sentences in a paragraph support the main idea, but some do not.

Read the passage. Then answer the questions below.

California, like other states, has many cities that are made up of many different communities. Each community is special in its own way. Communities are different from one another because of the people who live in them. In many communities, people have come from other countries. They practice their culture and do things in their traditional ways. Often, people move to a community for its schools.

1. Is the main idea stated in the paragraph? _____

2. Write the main idea of this paragraph. _____

_____

_____

3. Choose two details that support the main idea. _____

_____

_____

_____

4. Choose one detail that doesn't tell about the main idea. _____

_____

CA **R 2.5** Distinguish the main idea and supporting details in expository text.

Name _____

As you read *Coasting to California*, fill in the Main Idea and
Details Chart.

Main Idea _____

_____

Detail 1 _____

_____

Detail 2 _____

_____

↓

Summary _____

_____

_____

How does the information you wrote on the Main Idea and Details Chart
help you summarize *Coasting to California*?

R 2.5 Distinguish the main idea and supporting details
in expository text.

Coasting to California **97**
Grade 3/Unit 2

© Macmillan/McGraw-Hill

As I read, I will pay attention to my pronunciation and phrasing.

	There are many predictions about the future of
8	computers. Most people agree that progress will be made
17	in the way computers look and in the way people will use
29	them.
30	Some experts think that handheld computers will take
38	the place of books. Others think we'll have computers we
48	can wear. Some may hook onto your eyeglasses. This would
58	help pilots. They will be able to look at the sky and see
71	their gauges at the same time. Computers sewn in jackets
81	will let people keep track of their heart rate.
90	Computer screens that show 3-D images are predicted,
98	too. This will make game-playing far more exciting. 106

Comprehension Check

1. What is the main idea of this selection? **Main Idea and Details**

2. How do you think computers will help in the future? **Fact and Opinion**

	Words Read	–	Number of Errors	=	Words Correct Score
First Read		–		=	
Second Read		–		=	

© Macmillan/McGraw-Hill

CA **R 1.3** Read aloud narrative and expository text fluently and accurately and with appropriate pacing, intonation, and expression.

Name _____

You can find out whether a book has the information you need by looking at the different parts of the book:

title	**title page**	**table of contents**
preface	**chapter titles**	**headings**
subheadings	**index**	**glossary**

Answer each question below by writing the name of the book part.

1. Where would you look to find out the pages where you can find

   information on a specific topic? _____

   _____

2. Which parts of a book are usually printed in bold type? _____

   _____

3. Where might you find a short introduction to the book? _____

4. Where can you find the meaning of a difficult word? _____

5. Which part of a book lists the chapter titles, other book parts, and page

   numbers? _____

6. Which part of a book contains the title, the author's name, and the

   illustrator's name? _____

Description Writing Frame

A. Summarize *Coasting to California*. Use the Description Writing Frame below.

Chinese immigrants to the United States succeeded in **many ways**.

One way they succeeded is _____

_____

_____.

Another way they succeeded is _____

_____

_____

_____.

They also succeeded by _____

_____

_____

_____.

B. Rewrite the completed summary on another sheet of paper. Keep it as a model for writing a summary of an article or selection using this text structure.

CA R 2.0 Reading Comprehension

Name _____

Antonyms are words with opposite meanings. Sometimes, knowing the opposite of an unknown word can help you figure out the meaning of the new word. You can find antonyms listed in a **dictionary** and in a **thesaurus**. Sometimes the abbreviation *ant* is written before antonyms. Sometimes antonyms are printed in a different kind of type.

A. Read the dictionary and thesaurus entries for the word *ancient*. Then answer the questions below.

Thesaurus
ancient 1. very old, elderly **2.** early times **3.** old-fashioned *young, modern, new*
Dictionary
ancient (ān´ shənt) **1.** of long ago **2.** very old *ant* modern, young

1. How do you know which words in the thesaurus are antonyms?

_____

2. What antonyms for *ancient* are listed in the thesaurus?

_____

B. Use a dictionary or a thesaurus to write antonyms for the words below.

3. natural _____

4. harm _____

5. settle _____

© Macmillan/McGraw-Hill

CA **R 1.4** Use knowledge of antonyms, synonyms, homophones, and homographs to determine the meanings of words.

Coasting to California
Grade 3/Unit 2
101

scraped	scrubs	street	three
scratch	spray	strength	throne
screams	spread	strong	throw
screens	spree	thread	

Find and Circle

Where are the spelling words?

P	C	S	C	R	E	E	N	S	W	X
S	T	R	E	N	G	T	H	P	Z	K
C	S	B	M	F	J	H	U	R	V	T
R	C	W	S	T	H	R	E	A	D	H
U	R	S	P	L	Z	O	N	Y	Y	R
B	A	C	R	R	M	W	G	K	P	O
S	P	R	E	E	O	O	Q	W	N	N
S	E	E	A	S	T	R	O	N	G	E
H	D	A	D	D	T	H	R	E	E	Z
A	Q	M	H	S	T	R	E	E	T	U
F	V	S	C	R	A	T	C	H	S	C

LC 1.8 Spell correctly one-syllable words that have blends, contractions, compounds, orthographic patterns (e.g., *qu*, consonant doubling, changing the ending of a word from -*y* to -*ies* when forming the plural), and common homophones (e.g., *hair-hare*).

Name _____

A. Proofreading

There are six spelling mistakes in this TV broadcast. Circle the misspelled words. Write the words correctly on the lines below.

    Hello, everyone! This is Wendy Mills reporting live from the space shuttle liftoff. And what a sight it is. The shuttle is ready to go. The crowd is spreed out across a huge field. You can hear sckreems of excitement all around. NASA has set up three big schrenes that show what is going on inside the shuttle. The captain sits in a chair that is as big as a threwn! Outside, workers are lifting lots of heavy equipment. Wow, they sure must be stroon to carry all that weight. Any minute now they will thro the switch and the shuttle will take off. Stay tuned.

1. _____ 3. _____ 5. _____

2. _____ 4. _____ 6. _____

B. Writing Activity

Write a news report of an event you have seen. Use at least four spelling words in your description.

_____

_____

_____

_____

_____

_____

_____

_____

LC 1.8 Spell correctly one-syllable words that have blends, contractions, compounds, orthographic patterns (e.g., *qu*, consonant doubling, changing the ending of a word from *-y* to *-ies* when forming the plural), and common homophones (e.g., *hair-hare*).

Coasting to California
Grade 3/Unit 2
103

Name _____

- A few nouns are the same in both singular and plural forms.

Singular	Plural	Singular	Plural
sheep	sheep	fish	fish
deer	deer	trout	trout
buffalo	buffalo	salmon	salmon
moose	moose	scissors	scissors

Complete each sentence with the correct plural form of the noun in parentheses.

1. In the future, will (buffalo) _____ once again live in the Great Plains?

2. Will (deer) _____ still live in the forests or only in zoos?

3. These wild (sheep) _____ lived on their own in the hills.

4. Maybe (moose) _____ will survive in the north.

5. Large schools of (fish) _____ will feed millions of people.

6. Dams must allow (salmon) _____ to swim upstream.

7. People once fished for (trout) _____ for food.

8. Maybe someone will invent laser (scissors) _____ to cut paper.

© Macmillan/McGraw-Hill

CA   **LC 1.0** Written and Oral English Language Conventions

- Some nouns have special plural forms.
- A few nouns have the same singular and plural forms.

A. Proofread the paragraph for incorrect plural nouns. Circle each incorrect plural noun and write its correct form on the lines below.

What is in store for the future? I think our lifes will change. Maybe humans will have four foots. Then we will be able to run faster. Maybe we will have super-sharp toothes. Then we will use them instead of scissorses. Science will change the world in many ways. Tomato might be bigger than gooses. Mouses might be as strong as mooses. I think the world will be a very strange place!

_____   _____

_____   _____

_____   _____

_____   _____

B. Writing Activity

Write a personal narrative about something that you think will happen in the future. Use the irregular plural nouns that you learned.

_____

_____

_____

_____

_____

Writing Rubric

4 Excellent	3 Good	2 Fair	1 Unsatisfactory
Ideas and Content/Genre	Ideas and Content/Genre	Ideas and Content/Genre	Ideas and Content/Genre
Organization and Focus	Organization and Focus	Organization and Focus	Organization and Focus
Sentence Structure/Fluency	Sentence Structure/Fluency	Sentence Structure/Fluency	Sentence Structure/Fluency
Conventions	Conventions	Conventions	Conventions
Word Choice	Word Choice	Word Choice	Word Choice
Voice	Voice	Voice	Voice
Presentation	Presentation	Presentation	Presentation

CA W 1.0 Writing Strategies

Name _____

> You may see the letters **ch** at the beginning, middle, or end of a word. Say each of these words aloud: **ch**arge, mun**ch**ing, ben**ch**.
>
> You may see the letters **tch** at the middle or end of a word. Say these words aloud: stre**tch**, ma**tch**ing.

Look at the pictures below. Some pictures have the *ch* or *tch* sound in their names. Write the correct word on the line next to the question it answers.

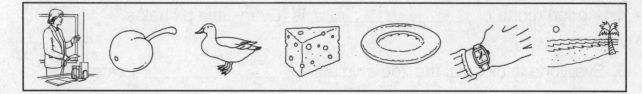

1. Which tells the time? _____

2. Which lays an egg? _____

3. Who instructs the class? _____

4. Which is covered in sand? _____

5. Which will help you measure a piece of ribbon? _____

6. Which melts on pizza? _____

7. Which is on the roof of a house that has a fireplace? _____

8. Which is put over a hole in your shirt? _____

CA **R 1.2** Decode regular multisyllabic words.

Complete each sentence with the vocabulary word that makes the most sense.

deserve	volunteers	tour
slogan	thrilled	

1. My friends and I are _____ at the city food bank.

2. We were _____ when we found out we were taking a field trip to the zoo.

3. My favorite _____ at the zoo is of the reptile house.

4. A good motto or _____ is "Every little bit helps."

5. Everyone thinks that the zoo animals _____ a safe place to live.

CA **R 1.0** Word Analysis, Fluency, and Systematic Vocabulary Development

Name _____

> Authors write for three main reasons: to entertain, to inform, or to persuade. Identifying an **author's purpose** in writing can tell readers what to expect.

Read the following passages. Tell the author's purpose for writing each one.

1. Animals do not eat the same food as humans, so some zoos sell food that you can feed to the animals. This food is part of their diet and is healthy for them. All animals need a proper diet to thrive.

   The author's purpose is _____.

2. Dad bought me a helium balloon. Suddenly, a monkey grabbed it from my hand. Off the monkey went, soaring into the air. A zookeeper sat on a giraffe to try and reach the silly monkey as it floated toward the clouds. That monkey has been grounded for a week!

   The purpose of this paragraph is _____.

3. Keep our zoos and nature parks clean. Use the trash cans that are placed throughout the parks. Animals can cut themselves on soda cans. Their necks can get caught in plastic rings. They can swallow objects that make them choke. We need everyone's help. We all lose if we don't protect our animals.

   The purpose of this paragraph is _____.

4. My class wanted to help out the community, so we planted a vegetable garden in an empty lot near our school. We grew tomatoes, beans, and squash. We gave all the vegetables to a local food bank.

   The purpose of this paragraph is _____.

CA **R 3.4** Determine the underlying theme or author's message in fiction and nonfiction text.

Name _____

As you read *Here's My Dollar*, fill in the Author's Purpose Chart.

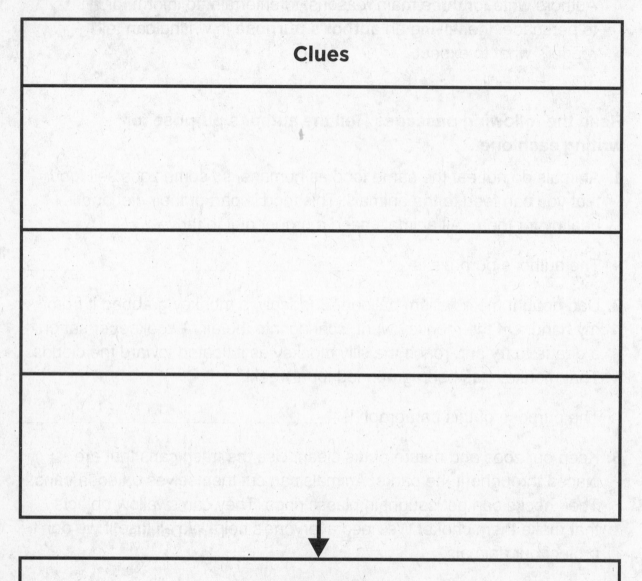

Clues

↓

Author's Purpose

How does the information your wrote in this Author's Purpose Chart help you monitor comprehension in *Here's My Dollar*?

 R 3.4 Determine the underlying theme or author's message in fiction and nonfiction text.

Name _____

As I read, I will pay attention to pacing.

	All playgrounds should be safe. But some of them are
10	not. Sometimes playground equipment breaks down. And
17	a broken piece of equipment can be dangerous. Sometimes
26	there are holes in the ground where children can trip and
37	fall. Kids, and even grownups, don't always recognize these
46	dangers.
47	One nine-year-old girl did spot dangers on a playground,
56	and she decided to take action. She came up with a
67	wonderful plan for making the playground safe. She's
75	Devan Hickey, a fun-loving girl who lives in Bryan, Ohio.
85	First Devan got all her facts together. Then she reported
95	her plan to a group of people in her community who could
107	help her. She also asked family and friends to help out. She
119	didn't give up until the playground was safe. Read her
129	story. 130

Comprehension Check

1. How do playgrounds become unsafe? **Main Idea and Details**

2. What steps did Devan follow to make a playground safer? **Chronological Order**

	Words Read	–	Number of Errors	=	Words Correct Score
First Read		–		=	
Second Read		–		=	

© Macmillan/McGraw-Hill

R 1.3 Read aloud narrative and expository text fluently and accurately and with appropriate pacing, intonation, and expression.

A **rhyme scheme** is the pattern of rhymes in a poem. In many poems there is **repetition**, or repeated words or phrases. A line that is repeated in a poem is called a **refrain**.

Read the poem. Underline the rhyming words and circle the refrain. Draw a square around words or phrases that show repetition.

Harbor

Down at the harbor
I did see,
A little gray mouse
as frisky as can be.

He scampered aboard a tugboat
and pulled a ship to sea.
He skittered aboard a motorboat
and helped the skiers ski.
He scuttled onto a fishing boat
and set the dolphins free.

Down at the harbor
I did see,
A little gray mouse
As frisky as can be.

The rhyme scheme of this poem is formed by rhyming the words in which

lines?_____

_____

Name _____

When you are reading, you sometimes come across an unknown word. You can often figure out its meaning by looking at **context clues,** the words and phrases around it. Some context clues will contain **examples** of the unfamiliar word. Example clues help readers better understand unfamiliar words by providing related information about those words.

Circle the example clues that help you understand each underlined word. Then write a possible definition for the underlined word. Use a dictionary to check your work.

1. The panel was made up of people of all <u>occupations</u>, including lawyers, physical therapists, and hairdressers.

   Meaning: _____

2. My best friend has two <u>siblings</u>, but I have four: two brothers and two sisters.

   Meaning: _____

3. From our window we could see many <u>structures</u> such as bridges, skyscrapers, and docks.

   Meaning: _____

4. Every cello, clarinet, trombone, and violin in the <u>orchestra</u> sounded beautiful during the grand finale.

   Meaning: _____

© Macmillan/McGraw-Hill

R 1.6 Use sentence and word context to find the meaning of unknown words.

Here's My Dollar • **Grade 3/Unit 2** 113

Name _____

cheese   stretch
chick   teacher
fish   them
hatch   thick
lunch   truth
much   whales
pathway   what
pitch

Find and Circle

Where are the spelling words?

T	H	I	C	K	W	L	W	S	Y
C	H	I	C	K	H	M	H	T	T
H	A	X	Y	R	A	V	A	R	E
E	F	I	S	H	T	P	L	E	A
E	T	H	E	M	E	I	E	T	C
S	Q	W	H	E	I	T	S	C	H
E	F	J	L	U	N	C	H	H	E
V	M	U	C	H	G	H	E	F	R
P	A	T	H	W	A	Y	N	G	S
H	A	T	C	H	T	R	U	T	H

© Macmillan/McGraw-Hill

LC 1.8 Spell correctly one-syllable words that have blends, contractions, compounds, orthographic patterns (e.g., *qu*, consonant doubling, changing the ending of a word from -y to -ies when forming the plural), and common homophones (e.g., *hair-hare*).

A. Proofreading

There are six spelling mistakes in the story. Circle the misspelled words. Write the words correctly on the lines below.

One day a wolf went out in the woods for a walk. He was hungry so he went looking for some lounch. He saw a ditch along the pathwye. He decided to hide there to wait for a nice fat mouse to come along.

The wolf sat in the hole for a long time. He was tired of waiting. He wished he could strech. Suddenly, he heard footsteps on the leaves on the path. He peeked out of the ditch and saw a little gray mouse dragging a bag.

The wolf leapt out of the hole and stood in front of the little mouse. Not very big, thought the wolf, but she will have to do. The mouse was scared, but then she had an idea.

"Wat about some cheez?" she said to the wolf. She reached into her bag and pulled out some cheese. The wolf looked at the thicke chunk of cheddar that the little mouse offered and then at the tiny size of the mouse.

"Thank you," said the wolf. "That would be great."

1. _____ 3. _____ 5. _____

2. _____ 4. _____ 6. _____

B. Writing Activity

Write a story about two animals meeting in the woods. Use four spelling words in your writing.

_____

_____

_____

_____

LC 1.8 Spell correctly one-syllable words that have blends, contractions, compounds, orthographic patterns (e.g., *qu*, consonant doubling, changing the ending of a word from -y to -ies when forming the plural), and common homophones (e.g., *hair-hare*).

Here's My Dollar • Grade 3/Unit 2 115

© Macmillan/McGraw-Hill

Name _____

> • Add an apostrophe (') to make most plural nouns possessive.
>   Example: planets' names
>
> • Add an apostrophe (') and **s** to form the possessive of plural nouns that do not end in *s*.
>   Example: people**'s** view

Write the possessive form of each underlined noun.

1. the size of the <u>rings</u>   the _____ size

2. the orbits of the <u>planets</u>   the _____ orbits

3. the telescope of the <u>children</u>   the _____ telescope

4. the tails of <u>comets</u>   the _____ tails

5. the distances of the <u>orbits</u>   the _____ distances

6. the lengths of the <u>days</u>   the _____ lengths

7. the speed of the <u>meteors</u>   the _____ speed

8. the patterns of the <u>stars</u>   the _____ patterns

9. the lights of the <u>pulsars</u>   the _____ lights

10. the music of the <u>spheres</u>   the _____ music

11. the glow of the <u>moons</u>   the _____ glow

12. the timings of the <u>eclipses</u>   the _____ timings

© Macmillan/McGraw-Hill

CA **LC 1.0** Written and Oral English Language Conventions

Name _____

• A possessive noun is a noun that shows who or what owns or has something.

A. Proofread the radio ad for incorrect possessive nouns. Circle each incorrect possessive noun and write its correct form on the lines below.

How long is Earths orbit   What are Saturns rings made of   how hot is the suns' surface?   Learn all this and more in "Our Super Solar System," a new show at the Museum of Science!

call 555-SOLAR for todays showtimes.   Mondays shows are sold out.   Ask about our special childrens's shows for schools and other groups   So get in orbit and come out to the Museum of Science!

_____

_____

B. Writing Activity

Rewrite the ad using correct forms of possessive nouns. Make sure every sentence begins with a capital letter and has an end mark.

_____

_____

_____

_____

_____

_____

_____

© Macmillan/McGraw-Hill

Name _____

1. Please list 2 ways to describe 2 different people who are both moving quickly without using the word "quickly".

_____

_____

2. Please describe 2 different words or expressions that mean moving slowly without using the word "slowly".

_____

_____

3. Please describe 2 different words or expressions that mean to throw something without using the word "throw".

_____

_____

Extra Practice: Write three different words or expressions for each of the following:

1. To want something
2. To dislike something
3. To work on something

_____

_____

_____

_____

© Macmillan/McGraw-Hill

CA   **W 1.0** Writing Strategies

Name _____

> **Contractions** are made when two words are put together in a shortened form. One or more letters are taken out to form a contraction. An apostrophe is used to take the place of the missing letter or letters.

A. Write the contraction for each pair of words.

1. I am _____

2. they are _____

3. do not _____

4. we will _____

5. we are _____

6. that is _____

7. did not _____

8. she is _____

9. have not _____

10. could not _____

B. Fill in the blank in each sentence with the correct contraction from the box.

| isn't | It's | We'd | They're | haven't |

11. _____ like you to visit our grandparents with us.

12. _____ building a new house in the country.

13. Since it _____ ready yet, they sleep in the old cabin.

14. They _____ hooked up electricity in the cabin.

15. _____ fun to swim in the pond and ride the horses.

Name _____

A. Fill in the blank with the word from the box that best completes each sentence.

leaky	owners	equipment
project	construction	appliances

1. New _____ are usually quieter than older washers and dishwashers.

2. The _____ pipe dripped all over the bathroom floor.

3. My cousins are the new _____ of the house across the street.

4. It will take a year of _____ to complete the new buildings.

5. We needed some large _____ to finish building the house.

6. It was a very big _____, and we all worked hard on it.

B. Choose four vocabulary words. Then use two of them in each sentence you write below.

7. _____

_____

8. _____

_____

CA **R 1.0** Word Analysis, Fluency, and Systematic Vocabulary Development

Name _____

An essential message or **theme** is the message or overall idea that the author wants to tell readers. The theme is not always stated. Sometimes readers need to identify the theme by reading carefully.

Read the passage. Answer the questions that follow.

Carrie was invited to a costume party, but she did not have a costume. She called her Aunt Harriet. She told Carrie to come right over. Aunt Harriet had dozens of costumes. In fact, she had a huge collection because she saved every costume she had ever worn to a party. She still had costumes that she had worn in high school! Aunt Harriet was sure Carrie would find something to wear. She was right!

1. Put a check next to the theme of the passage.

   ____ Aunt Harriet enjoys hearing from Carrie.

   ____ Never throw anything away; it may be worth a lot of money.

   ____ Being resourceful pays off.

2. Was the theme stated or unstated? _____

3. What information in the passage helped you decide your answer?

   _____

   _____

4. Write a short paragraph that has a theme about helping others.

   _____

   _____

   _____

   _____

R 3.4 Determine the underlying theme or author's message in fiction and nonfiction text.

As you read *A Castle on Viola Street*, fill in the Theme Map.

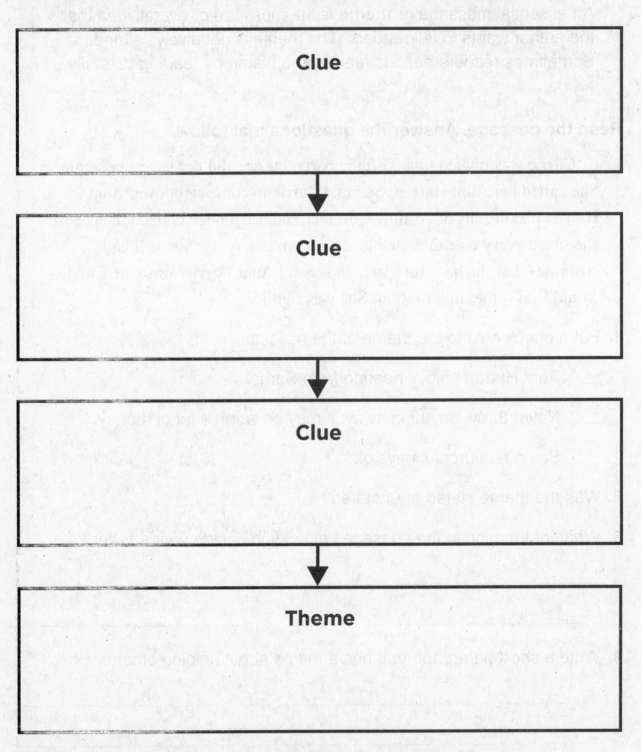

Clue

Clue

Clue

Theme

How does the information you wrote in this Theme Map help you
understand the essential message in *A Castle on Viola Street*?

CA R 3.4 Determine the underlying theme or author's message in fiction
and nonfiction text.

As I read, I will pay attention to inflection and punctuation.

	Aunt Claire was the owner of a store called The Junque
11	Shoppe. That was a fancy way of saying that she sold junk.
23	Some of the things in the store were antiques, but others
34	were just old.
37	Aunt Claire did give good presents, though.
44	This time she had a pretty box filled with old beads for
56	Susan. For four-year-old Emma she had a stuffed alligator.
65	The minute Emma saw the alligator she forgot all about
75	saying goodbye to her mom and dad. "Fluffy can sit on my
87	bed," she announced.
90	"Fluffy isn't a good name for an alligator," Susan said.
100	"Don't upset your sister," her mom warned.
107	Susan rolled her eyes. She was just trying to be helpful.
118	Mom and dad finally said their goodbyes and left. After
128	dinner, Emma sat down to watch a video about dinosaurs.
138	Susan looked at her beads. 143

Comprehension Check

1. How does Emma feel about her stuffed alligator? **Plot Development**

2. Why does Susan think the name Fluffy is not a good name for an alligator? **Plot Development**

	Words Read	–	Number of Errors	=	Words Correct Score
First Read		–		=	
Second Read		–		=	

© Macmillan/McGraw-Hill

R 1.3 Read aloud narrative and expository text fluently and accurately and with appropriate pacing, intonation, and expression.

Textbooks often have special features to help you understand what you are reading. Each chapter usually begins with an introduction that prepares you for what to look for as you read. Other features, such as headings, boldface type, and picture captions, can help you pick out important words and concepts.

Read the passage below and answer the questions.

Foods Around the World

Some foods have different names in different countries. Think about your favorite foods at home. You may be surprised to learn what they are called in other countries.

Confusing Food Names

A **biscuit** in England is not the same as a biscuit in America. A biscuit in England is called a *cookie* in the United States. In England a pie is called **flan,** french fries are called *chips,* and potato chips are called *crisps.*

1. Which words begin the introduction? _____

2. What is special about the words *biscuit* and *flan*?

   a. They are in boldface type.   **b.** They are italicized.

3. Why do you think the words *biscuit* and *flan* appear the way they do?

   _____

4. Why are the words "Foods Around the World" in the largest type on the page?

   _____

5. What words make up the heading? _____

CA **R 2.1** Use titles, tables of contents, chapter headings, glossaries, and indexes to locate information in text.

Name _____

When you see an unfamiliar word while reading, using the words around it can help you figure out its meaning. These words are **context clues** and can be synonyms, antonyms, or examples.

Read each sentence. Use context clues to decide what each underlined word means. Circle the correct answer, then write the correct meaning on the line.

1. The workers will <u>renovate</u>, or fix up, the oldest buildings.

   In the sentence, *renovate* means _____.

   a. improve by repairing   **b.** study plans   **c.** tear down

2. The plumber was <u>frustrated</u> when he could not fix the leaky faucet.

   In the sentence, *frustrated* means _____.

   a. successful   **b.** discouraged   **c.** very jolly

3. The owner came to the building site <u>disguised</u> as a worker so no one would know he was there.

   In the sentence, *disguised* means _____.

   a. not ready   **b.** not forgotten   **c.** changed one's looks to hide

4. The neighbors may <u>oppose</u> and complain about the construction of a building that is much larger than the others.

   In the sentence, *oppose* means _____.

   a. carry too far   **b.** whisper about   **c.** be against

5. The owners were <u>ecstatic</u> when the real estate agent turned over the keys to their new house.

   In the sentence, *ecstatic* means _____.

   a. delighted   **b.** frightened   **c.** very shy

© Macmillan/McGraw-Hill

CA **R 1.6** Use sentence and word context to find the meaning of unknown words.

Name _____

Using the Word Study Steps

1. LOOK at the word.

2. SAY the word aloud.

3. STUDY the letters in the word.

4. WRITE the word.

5. CHECK the word.
   Did you spell the word right?
   If not, go back to step 1.

Circle the words that make up the contraction in each row.

1. won't   were not   will not   we will

2. they're   they are   they would   they can

3. I've   I am   I shall   I have

4. isn't   he is   is not   is too

5. she'd   she is   she will   she would

6. wouldn't   would not   he would   would also

7. there's   there are   there will be there is

8. that's   that is   that are   that will be

9. wasn't   was it   was not   was to be

10. we'll   we will   we are   we have

CA LC 1.8 Spell correctly one-syllable words that have blends, contractions, compounds, orthographic patterns (e.g., *qu*, consonant doubling, changing the ending of a word from -*y* to -*ies* when forming the plural), and common homophones (e.g., *hair-hare*).

A. **There are six spelling mistakes in the journal entry below. Circle the misspelled words. Write the words correctly on the lines below.**

I saw a show on TV about a big storm that ruined a town. The people couldnt stay in their homes. I'v never seen whole houses blown down!

My family wanted to help. At first, we din't know what we could do. Then we learned that we could help rebuild houses. My dad is a teecher and doesn't work in the summer. So, my whole family went to build a house. It it really wuzn't that hard and we had lots of fun. Wee'l never forgot that summer!

1. _____   4. _____

2. _____   5. _____

3. _____   6. _____

B. **Write a paragraph about a time you helped other people. Use at least four spelling words in your paragraph.**

_____

_____

_____

_____

_____

_____

LC 1.8 Spell correctly one-syllable words that have blends, contractions, compounds, orthographic patterns (e.g., *qu*, consonant doubling, changing the ending of a word from -*y* to -*ies* when forming the plural), and common homophones (e.g., *hair-hare*).

- Two sentences can be combined by joining two nouns with *and*.
  - Separate: Teachers help children.
                 Teachers help adults.
  - Combined: Teachers help children and adults.

- Some nouns are the objects of sentences. Sometimes two objects can be joined with *and*.
  - Separate: The book described tigers.
                 The book described lions.
  - Combined: The book described tigers and lions.

**Combine the sentences. Use *and* to join the underlined nouns.
Write the new sentences.**

1. Authors write books. Authors write short stories.

   _____

2. Authors imagine places. Authors imagine characters.

   _____

3. An author visited Ms. Green's class. An author visited Mr. Finn's class.

   _____

4. The author portrayed imaginary people. The author portrayed real people.

   _____

5. The author discussed her books. The author discussed her characters.

   _____

6. The author heard our stories. The author heard our poems.

   _____

© Macmillan/McGraw-Hill

CA LC 1.0 Written and Oral English Language Conventions

- Two sentences can be combined by joining two nouns with *and*.
- Some nouns are the subjects of sentences.
- Sometimes two subjects can be joined with *and*.
- Some nouns are the objects of sentences. Sometimes two objects can be joined with *and*.

A. Proofread the book review. Find two pairs of sentences that can be combined. Then write the new combined sentences on the lines below.

    I just finished the book first year. It is about Nicole. It is about Laurie. They are twins it is their first year at boarding school. the girls had real-life problems School wasn't easy. they wanted to go home. Then Nicole made new friends. Then Laurie made new friends. They had fun.

    I couldn't put this book down. I would tell others to read this book.

_____

_____

B. Writing Activity

Rewrite the book review with the new combined sentences. Make sure all sentences begin with a capital letter and end with an end mark. Make sure that book titles are written correctly.

_____

_____

_____

_____

_____

Name _____

1. Please underline the verbs in the following sentences:

I said goodbye.

I came to school.

I ate lunch in the cafeteria.

2. Now, rewrite each sentence so that it shows more about how YOU did these things.

_____

_____

_____

_____

_____

_____

_____

Extra Practice: Do the same activity for the following sentences.

I like ice cream.

I went to my friend's house.

CA W 1.0 Writing Strategies

Name _____

> The sound /ûr/ can be spelled in different ways. For example:
>
> **er** in the word *her*   **ear** in the word *learn*
> **ir** in the word *skirt*   **ur** in the word *nurse*

A. Answer each question with a word from the word box that has the /ûr/ sound.

large	dart	birth	dirty	burn	search	scared
first	learn	guard	fern	early	purse	hurry

1. When my room is _____ my mom makes me clean it before I can play outside.

2. We always get to the museum _____ so we don't have to wait in line.

3. I am usually the _____ to wake up. I like to read before the house gets too noisy.

4. Sarah can never find her wallet in her _____ because it is filled with other things.

5. The scientists found nothing in their _____ for dinosaur bones in the desert.

B. Choose two other words from the box that have the /ûr/ sound and use them in the same sentence. Underline the words.

6. _____

_____

© Macmillan/McGraw-Hill

Name _____

A. Use the following words to complete each sentence below.

| proper   talented   useful   single   excitement   acceptance |

1. A snow shovel is the most _____ tool for clearing snow off a sidewalk.

2. The _____ ballet dancer moved gracefully across the stage.

3. The writer was thrilled when he received a letter of _____ for his poem.

4. Eating breakfast is the _____ most important part of the morning.

5. We were careful to use _____ manners at the table.

6. Our _____ grew as we waited for the author's plane to land.

B. Write the definitions for the following words.

7. acceptance _____

_____

8. talented _____

_____

9. excitement _____

_____

10. proper _____

_____

CA R 1.0 Word Analysis, Fluency, and Systematic Vocabulary Development

Name _____

There are three common purposes or reasons why authors write: to **inform,** or give facts to readers; to **persuade,** or convince readers to believe or do something; to **entertain,** or tell a good story.

Read each passage. Circle the author's purpose. Then explain your answer.

Writing is my favorite thing to do when I get home from school. You should definitely try it. After school go home and just write about your thoughts for the day. Who knows, maybe your thoughts will turn into a story!

1. The author's purpose is to:

   a. persuade   **b.** entertain   **c.** inform

2. because _____

Getting a book published is a long process. You have to write your story and then send it to a publisher. The publisher will decide if they like the story you wrote and then will publish it. Sometimes publishers do not like the story and you have to start the process over again.

3. The author's purpose is to:

   a. persuade   **b.** entertain   **c.** inform

4. because _____

The funniest thing happened to me on my walk home from school. This cat in a tiny airplane flew over my head. I chased the plane and it landed in someone's backyard. Then I noticed a little boy with a remote that was flying the small plane. Turns out the cat was not real!

5. The author's purpose is to:

   a. persuade   **b.** entertain   **c.** inform

6. because _____

© Macmillan/McGraw-Hill

Name _____

As you read *Author: A True Story*, fill in the Author's Purpose Chart.

Clues

↓

Author's Purpose

How does the information you wrote in the Author's Purpose Chart help you summarize *Author: A True Story*?

CA R 2.0 Reading Comprehension

As I read, I will pay attention to sentence length.

	Elwyn Brooks White was born on July 11, 1899. He
10	was the baby in his family. He had three sisters and two
22	brothers. His brother Stanley taught him to read before
31	he even started school.
35	All six White children learned music. After dinner, the
44	Whites played music together.
48	They also did their homework. Mr. and Mrs. White had
58	been too poor to stay in school. But they wanted their
69	children to get a good education.
75	The Whites lived in Mount Vernon, a city near New
85	York City. Mount Vernon was more like a rural town in
96	those days. A boy could still find many wild animals.
106	White always had a dog and lots of other pets. 116

Comprehension Check

1. What did the Whites do for entertainment? **Main Idea and Details**

2. How did Mr. and Mrs. White feel about school? **Make Inferences**

	Words Read	–	Number of Errors	=	Words Correct Score
First Read		–		=	
Second Read		–		=	

© Macmillan/McGraw-Hill

CA **R 1.3** Read aloud narrative and expository text fluently and accurately and with appropriate pacing, intonation, and expression.

Onomatopoeia is the use of a word that is spelled to mimic the sound it describes. For example, the words *honk* and *beep* describe the sounds of a horn; *splash* is the sound water makes.

Rhythm is the sound pattern of a poem. Some syllables are stressed, or said with more strength. The stressed and unstressed syllables give the poem its rhythm. The stressed syllables are in dark print in the examples below.
Example: **Ro**ses are **red**. **Vi**olets are **blue**.

A. Use the examples of onomatopoeia in the box to describe each phrase below. Some words will not be used at all.

screech	crash	squeak	buzz	sizzle	boom

1. something breaks as it falls to the floor _____

2. something explodes _____

3. a swarm of bees _____

4. tires stopping quickly _____

B. Write a couplet, a poem with two lines. Use at least one example of onomatopoeia in your poem. Read your poem aloud and listen for the rhythm. Then underline the stressed syllables in each line.

_____

_____

© Macmillan/McGraw-Hill

CA **R 3.5** Define figurative language (e.g., simile, metaphor, hyperbole, personification) and identify its use in literary works.

When you read an unfamiliar word, you can use **context clues,** or the words or sentences around the word, to figure out its meaning.

Read the sentences below. Use context clues to figure out the meaning of the underlined words. Write the meaning on the line.

1. We waited in line to get an autograph. The writer sat at a small table signing copies of her book.

   autograph means _____

2. The illustrator of the book was nearly as famous as the author. He was known for his detailed pen and ink drawings.

   illustrator means _____

3. I sent my completed book to a publisher. The publisher decided to print my book.

   publisher means _____

4. Every day I eagerly checked the mailbox for a letter that didn't come. I was very frustrated by the delay.

   frustrated means _____

5. The fireworks quickly fizzled out. The rain made it hard for them to burn.

   fizzled means _____

6. The author was very proud of her book. She showed all her friends the acceptance letter.

   proud means _____

© Macmillan/McGraw-Hill

CA R 1.6 Use sentence and word context to find the meaning of unknown words.

Name _____

Using the Word Study Steps

1. LOOK at the word.
2. SAY the word aloud.
3. STUDY the letters in the word.
4. WRITE the word.
5. CHECK the word.
   Did you spell the word right?
   If not, go back to step 1.

earn	purr
firm	serve
first	third
girls	turns
herds	word
learn	world
nurse	worth
perch	

Find and Circle

Where are the spelling words?

W	O	R	L	D	Z	P	X	Q	C
O	C	F	G	C	N	U	R	S	E
R	D	A	W	E	G	R	E	J	A
T	H	I	R	D	I	R	I	P	R
H	E	J	U	I	R	Q	S	E	N
W	R	C	F	T	L	E	A	R	N
F	D	U	I	O	S	P	D	C	D
I	S	E	R	V	E	K	L	H	F
R	A	K	S	G	T	U	R	N	S
M	A	A	T	J	W	O	R	D	R

© Macmillan/McGraw-Hill

Name _____

A. There are six spelling mistakes in this essay. Circle the misspelled words. Write the words correctly on the lines below.

Exploring Ecosystems

A lot of people want to explore space, but I want to explore this wurld. There is so much to see and do right here on this planet. I want to lern as much as I can about the deserts and oceans here on earth. I want to study hurds of camels as they cross the Sahara. I want to observe eagles as they pirch on a mountain. It will be difficult, but it will be wurth it. I may even be the furst person to discover a new ecosystem!

1. _____   4. _____

2. _____   5. _____

3. _____   6. _____

B. Writing Activity

Imagine that you are an explorer. Write about a new ecosystem that you just found for the first time. Use at least four spelling words.

_____

_____

_____

_____

_____

_____

_____

© Macmillan/McGraw-Hill

LC 1.8 Spell correctly one-syllable words that have blends, contractions, compounds, orthographic patterns (e.g., *qu*, consonant doubling, changing the ending of a word from -*y* to -*ies* when forming the plural), and common homophones (e.g., *hair-hare*).

Author: A True Story • Grade 3/Unit 3 139

Name _____

- An **action verb** is a word that shows action.
  Some action verbs tell about actions that are hard to see.
  Carly <u>enjoys</u> parties.
  She <u>invites</u> friends for lunch.

Here is a list of action verbs. Choose an action verb to finish each sentence. Write the verb on the line.

answers	sits
eats	slices
greets	smiles
makes	tastes
sets	works

1. Carly _____ the door.

2. She _____ the guests.

3. Everyone _____ together in the kitchen.

4. Ray _____ the tomatoes with a knife.

5. Tracy _____ the sandwiches.

6. Brian _____ the table.

7. The whole group _____ down.

8. Everyone _____ lunch.

9. The food _____ good.

10. Carly _____ happily.

CA **LC 1.3** Identify and use past, present, and future verb tenses properly in writing and speaking.

A. Proofread the story. Start by finding and circling the action verbs.

It is the day after Thanksgiving. The same thing happens on this day every year. Grandma gets up early then she goes to the kitchen. She takes the leftovers from Thanksgiving and uses them to make soup. She trims the turkey off the bone I cut up the vegetables. We pour in some water and stir everything around. George says he can't eat another thing. then he eats the rest of the pie and stuffing.

The soup cooks in a big pot on the stove. It smells good. Later in the day, our cousins visit us. We'll have the soup then we'll say again how we can't eat another thing. We'll enjoy a good day.

B. Rewrite the story. Make sure commas are used correctly. Put in capital letters and end marks where they are needed.

_____

_____

_____

_____

_____

_____

_____

_____

_____

_____

LC 1.3 Identify and use past, present, and future verb tenses properly in writing and speaking.

Author: A True Story • Grade 3/Unit 3   141

Name _____

1. Please fill in the blank:

Every sentence starts with a _____.

2. Now, read the following sentences.

the phone was ringing all morning long. steve would hang up
with one person when it would ring again. he wondered how
long it would last.

3. Circle the words that should start with capital letters.

Extra Practice: Do the same exercise using the following sentences.

molly wished that she didn't have to go to the dentist. she dreaded
dentist appointments more than anything in the world. she would rather
do a book report than go to the dentist. the only good thing about it is
that once it's over, she doesn't have to go again for another year.

When the letter *a* is followed by *r*, it usually stands for the **/är/** sound you hear in *barn*. When the letter *o* is followed by *r*, it usually stands for the **/ôr/** sound you hear in *horn*. Other words with the vowel sounds /är/ and /ôr/ include *farm* and *shore*.

A. Fill in the missing letters *ar* or *or* in each blank to make a word that makes sense in the sentence.

1. I received a birthday c _____ d in the mail from my grandmother.

2. When we have a lot of people over for dinner, I always go to the

   st _____ e with my mother to help her.

3. When my dog wants to be let in the house, she b _____ ks at the back door.

4. The walls were painted d _____ k blue.

5. When it is nice outside, I like to go to the p _____ k with my sister and swing on the swings.

6. Jennifer is so sm _____ rt, she can solve hard puzzles.

B. Write a sentence to show the meaning of the following words.

7. born _____

8. part _____

9. more _____

10. cart _____

R 1.1 Know and use complex word families when reading (e.g., *-ight*) to decode unfamiliar words.

Dear Juno • Grade 3/Unit 3   **143**

Read the story. Fill in the blanks with the correct words.

crackle	announced	soared
starry	noticed	

The Move

I couldn't believe it when my father _____ we would be moving to Oregon. My best friend Jacob was even more upset. We promised to stay in touch, but we knew it wouldn't be the same as seeing each other face to face.

A month later, as our plane _____ from New York to our new home, the _____ of my little brother's pretzel bag woke me. I looked out at the _____ night sky and came up with a great idea. If Jacob can't see me face to face, I'll just have to send him a photograph. "Perfect," I thought as I held out my arms in front of me to snap my own picture. The next day I sent it to him.

One week later I _____ that the mail carrier had delivered an envelope from Jacob to me! Inside was his picture and a letter. If we can't see each other face to face, at least we can see each other face to picture.

CA R 1.0 Word Analysis, Fluency, and Systematic Vocabulary Development

Name _____

The **characters** are the people and animals in a story. The **setting** is where and when the story takes place. The **plot** is the important events in the beginning, middle, and end of the story.

Read the letter and answer the questions below.

Dear Jesse,

   Wait until I tell you what happened in school today! Remember that new boy, Jake? Well, it turns out he is not as mean as I thought he was.

   Today, a little girl was crying in the playground. Her ball was stuck on a tree branch. Guess what Jake did? He actually climbed the tree and got the ball for her. She didn't even ask him for help. He gave it to her and actually played until the end of recess. I never expected him to be nice. Maybe I should have gotten to know Jake before I judged him.

Your friend,

Helen

1. What characters did Helen write about? _____

2. What are the important events that help Helen change her mind about

Jake? _____

_____

_____

3. Where did Jake show his true personality? _____

4. How has Helen's opinion of Jake changed? _____

_____

_____

As you read *Dear Juno*, fill in the Character Web.

How does the information you wrote in this Character Web help you analyze story structure in *Dear Juno*?

CA R 2.0 Reading Comprehension

Name _____

As I read, I will pay attention to dialogue and punctuation.

	A week earlier, Mr. Wilson had announced that his class
10	was going to become pen pals with a classroom of students
21	in Africa.
23	Mr. Wilson rolled up the map. He picked up a piece of
35	chalk. "Please raise your hand if you know what you'd like
46	to say in the letter."
51	He wrote a greeting at the top of the chalkboard.
61	Dear students of Mr. Addo's class,
67	Danny's hand shot up. "We're very excited to be your
77	pen pals," he said.
81	Mr. Wilson wrote those words under the greeting.
89	Then Sonya raised her hand. "It's autumn here in Iowa.
99	What is the weather like now in Ghana?" 107

Comprehension Check

1. To which country in Africa is Mr. Wilson's class going to send a letter?
Plot Development

2. What are some other things Mr. Wilson's class might want to know about
or share with Mr. Addo's class? **Plot Development**

© Macmillan/McGraw-Hill

	Words Read	–	Number of	=	Words
First Read		–		=	
Second Read		–		=	

CA **R 1.3** Read aloud narrative and expository text fluently and accurately
and with appropriate pacing, intonation, and expression.

A **time line** shows an order of events and the years they happened. To read a time line, read the year, then read the event or information connected to it.

Use the time line to answer the questions below.

Approximate Number of Households with Cable Television

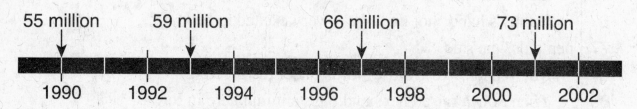

1. About how many households had cable television in 1990?

_____

2. In which year did about 66 million households have cable television?

_____

3. About how many households had cable television in 1993?

_____

4. About how many more households had cable television in 1997 than in 1990?

_____

5. Between what years did the number of households with cable television increase by 14 million?

_____

CA R 2.1 Use titles, tables of contents, chapter headings, glossaries, and indexes to locate information in text.

Context clues are words or sentences before or after an unfamiliar word. Use them to help you figure out the meaning of the unfamiliar word.

Read the sentences. Circle the context clues that help you understand the meaning of the underlined word. Write the meaning of each word.

1. Because it took so long to ride across the country, only **rapid** horseback riders rode for the Pony Express.

   Rapid means _____

2. The **memorandum** was left on the notepad next to the phone.

   Memorandum means _____

3. The plane we took to visit our aunt **ascended** quickly up to the sky.

   Ascended means _____

4. I received an email from a **random** person I had never heard of.

   Random means _____

5. The **chat** between the two friends ended when Tim hung up the phone.

   Chat means _____

6. Blue whales are **mammoth** and can grow to one hundred feet.

   Mammoth means _____

CA **R 1.6** Use sentence and word context to find the meaning of unknown words.

Dear Juno • Grade 3/Unit 3   149

Name _____

bark	shorts
carve	sour
chore	sport
hard	storms
porch	story
pour	wore
sharks	yard
sharp	

Find and Circle

Where are the spelling words?

S	H	A	R	K	S	B	S	B	N	Z
P	O	R	C	H	T	U	T	H	M	S
O	U	U	I	Z	O	P	O	U	R	H
R	Y	X	S	O	R	E	R	P	Y	O
T	Q	N	B	S	M	W	Y	C	A	R
V	C	B	V	D	S	Q	D	A	R	T
S	H	A	R	P	H	H	A	R	D	S
Z	Q	R	C	L	C	E	R	V	T	A
F	E	K	A	C	H	O	R	E	B	E
O	W	W	O	R	E	L	J	J	N	L

LC 1.8 Spell correctly one-syllable words that have blends, contractions, compounds, orthographic patterns (e.g., *qu*, consonant doubling, changing the ending of a word from *-y* to *-ies* when forming the plural), and common homophones (e.g., *hair-hare*).

Name _____

A. There are five spelling mistakes in this paragraph. Circle the misspelled words. Write the words correctly on the lines below.

Everyone in my family has a choar at dinner time. Tonight we are having a big turkey dinner, so we all have a lot of work to do. Mom is in charge of the gravy. My job is to set the table. I put out the plates and napkins. I also porr milk into all the glasses. Mike is my big brother, so he is in charge of cutting the bread. He has to use a shorpp knife. Dad has the best job of all. It is hord, but he loves it. He has to karve the turkey!

1. _____   4. _____

2. _____   5. _____

3. _____

B. Writing Activity

Write about a chore you must do each day. Use at least three spelling words in your description.

_____

_____

_____

_____

_____

_____

_____

LC 1.8 Spell correctly one-syllable words that have blends, contractions, compounds, orthographic patterns (e.g., *qu*, consonant doubling, changing the ending of a word from -y to -ies when forming the plural), and common homophones (e.g., *hair-hare*).

Dear Juno • **Grade 3/Unit 3**   151

- A verb in the **present tense** tells what happens now.
- A present-tense verb must **agree** with its subject.
- Add -*s* to most verbs if the subject is singular.
- Add -*es* to verbs that end in *s*, *ch*, *sh*, *x*, or *z* if the subject is singular.
- Change *y* to *i* and add -*es* to verbs that end with a consonant and *y*.
- Do not add -*s* or -*es* to a present-tense verb when the subject is plural or *I* or *you*.

  She <u>wishes</u>.   The ink <u>dries</u>.
  They <u>wish</u>.   The papers <u>dry</u>.

For each verb below, write the form that agrees with the subject given.

1. carry   Ann _____.

2. pitch   Mike _____.

3. wash   We _____.

4. fix   They _____.

5. guess   Flora _____.

6. push   We _____.

7. match   They _____.

8. mix   Kim _____.

9. squash   She _____.

10. fly   Don _____.

11. snatch   They _____.

12. toss   Lee _____.

© Macmillan/McGraw-Hill

CA **LC 1.0** Written and Oral English Language Conventions

Name _____

A. Proofread the paragraph. Circle any verbs that do not agree with their subjects.

Dad tell us riddles when we go on car trips. The riddles makes the ride more fun. They sounds easy at first. There is always a trick, though. He ask how many letters are in the alphabet. We tell him twenty-six. Then, Dad laugh at us. He say, "Count again." There are only eleven letters in the word alphabet! When we complains, Dad gives us a hint. "Think first, he explains. Sometimes Kris hurry up with her answer. He ask, "Are you sure?" When I rushes my guess, he tells me, "Listen again." Now we makes better guesses. Sometimes we even gets them right!

B. Rewrite the paragraph. Write the verbs so that they agree with their subjects.

_____

_____

_____

_____

_____

_____

_____

_____

_____

1. Fill in the blanks. You may look back at your last journal entry if you need help remembering the answers.

   Every sentence ends with _____.

   You can use a _____, a _____, or
   a _____.

2. Now, read the sentences below and add the correct punctuation mark at the end.

   a. Tom drove us to the movies

   b. When did you get that haircut

   c. Look out

   d. Who is that guy

   e. Those clouds look pretty stormy

   f. The phone is ringing

Extra Practice: Do the same exercise with these sentences:

   a. May I go to the restroom, please

   b. Yesterday I was late for school

   c. Stop it

   d. Do you think this picture is nice

   e. I was excited to finish my book

   f. Fall is my favorite season

CA W 1.0 Writing Strategies

Name _____

A **prefix** is a word part that can be added to the beginning of base words to make new words with different meanings.

Prefix	Meaning	Base Word	New Word	New Meaning
re-	again	re + build	rebuild	build again
un-	not or opposite	un + able	unable	not able
pre-	before or ahead	pre + heat	preheat	heat before
mis-	wrong	mis + count	miscount	count wrong

Read each sentence and write a prefix that makes sense for each word. Then write the meaning of the new word.

1. I didn't get your e-mail because you _____spelled my name.

   _____

2. I was able to _____pay for my ticket, so I did not wait in line.

   _____

3. My mom is _____able to send text messages, so I do it for her.

   _____

4. Please _____read my e-mail and then send me an answer.

   _____

5. I forgot to _____plug my computer when I went away for the weekend.

   _____

6. I _____placed your phone number and e-mail address, so please send

   them again.

   _____

© Macmillan/McGraw-Hill

R 1.8 Use knowledge of prefixes (e.g., *un-*, *re-*, *pre-*, *bi-*, *mis-*, *dis-*) and suffixes (e.g., *-er*, *-est*, *-ful*) to determine the meaning of words.

A. Read the story. Then fill in each blank with the correct word from the box.

record	focus	estimate

I have been reading an online almanac. Scientists predict

that our area will be hit with a big snowstorm next winter. They

_____ that we will receive about 36 inches of

snow. That's three feet of snow! I wonder if the snowstorm will set a

_____ for the most snow in one storm. I told my

mom about the storm predicted for next winter. She said that I should

_____ on my homework that's due tomorrow. She

doesn't want to hear about storms that might happen a long time from now!

B. Use clues in the story to write the definitions of the vocabulary words. Check your definitions with a dictionary.

1. record _____

2. focus _____

3. estimate _____

CA R 1.0 Word Analysis, Fluency, and Systematic Vocabulary Development

Name _____

Like someone in real life, a character in a story may have a
difficulty or **problem**. What the character does to solve the
difficulty or the problem is called the **solution**.

Read the passage, and answer the questions about it.

Lara wanted to call her grandmother to thank her for the birthday
gift, but her cell phone wasn't in her backpack. Lara took her room apart,
but she couldn't find it anywhere. Then she had an idea. She asked her
neighbor Andrew to call her cell phone number. Andrew called, and Lara
listened for the ring. She heard the ring coming from the family room.
Lara jumped up and down after she discovered her phone under a pillow.

1. What problem does Lara have?

_____

_____

2. What steps does Lara take to solve her problem?

_____

_____

_____

3. Why does Lara jump up and down?

_____

_____

4. What word would you use to describe Lara's plan for finding her phone?

_____

© Macmillan/McGraw-Hill

R 2.6 Extract appropriate and significant information from the text,
including problems and solutions.

Messaging Mania
Grade 3/Unit 3

157

Name _____

As you read *Messaging Mania*, fill in the Problem and Solution Chart.

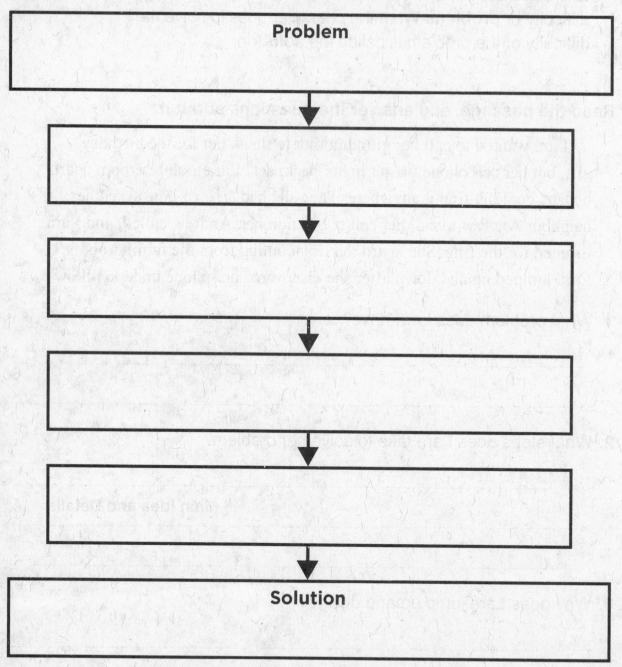

Problem

Solution

How does the information you wrote in this Problem and Solution
Chart help you better understand *Messaging Mania*?

CA **R 2.6** Extract appropriate and significant information from the text,
including problems and solutions.

Name _____

As I read, I will pay attention to my pronunciation and phrasing.

	When something breaks on the space station, what does
9	the crew do? They fix it. To repair the outside of the space
22	station, they must take a spacewalk.
28	The temperature in space can be very hot or very cold.
38	Astronauts wear spacesuits for protection. Their suits also
47	provide air, since there is no oxygen in space.
57	What happens if gravity pulls astronauts away during a
65	spacewalk? They use a jet-pack "life jacket" to easily fly
75	back to the station.
79	Each year, new tools make the job of fixing the space
90	station a bit easier. A new kind of radio lets up to five
103	people talk at one time. Heaters help keep fingers warm.
113	New lights on the space helmets shine on dim and dark
124	work areas. 126

Comprehension Check

1. How does the spacesuit protect the astronauts? **Main Idea and Details**

2. How do new tools make fixing the space station easier? **Main Idea and Details**

	Words Read	−	Number of Errors	=	Words Correct Score
First Read		−		=	
Second Read		−		=	

CA R 1.3 Read aloud narrative and expository text fluently and accurately
and with appropriate pacing, intonation, and expression.

The library contains many resources.

- You can look up a topic, author, and title online in the **electronic card catalog** to find out whether the library has the book you are looking for.
- A **telephone directory** gives addresses and telephone numbers of people and businesses. The directory may be in a book or online.
- **Newspapers** and **magazines** offer information about people, places, and things. You can learn about events that have just happened. Newspapers and periodicals are available in print or online.

Complete each of the following statements with the name of the resource you would use.

1. Sam's computer is broken, and he wants to find the number of the local

   computer store. He should check the _____.

2. Mr. Chan wants to find an article about recent whale migration in the

   Pacific Ocean. He should check a science _____.

3. Many people in my town want to read about the results of yesterday's

   election. They should check the _____.

4. I want to know if the library has a specific book about grizzly bears. I will

   check the _____.

© Macmillan/McGraw-Hill

CA **W 1.3** Understand the structure and organization of various reference materials (e.g., dictionary, thesaurus, atlas, encyclopedia).

Name _____

Problem and Solution Writing Frame

A. Summarize *Messaging Mania*. Use the Problem and Solution Writing Frame below.

Instant messaging has resulted in several **problems**.

One problem is _____ because _____

_____

_____

_____.

Another problem is _____ because _____

_____

_____

_____.

The **solution** to these problems is _____

_____

_____

_____.

B. Rewrite the completed summary on another sheet of paper. Keep it as a model for writing a summary of an article or selection using this text structure.

Homographs are words that are spelled the same but have more than one meaning. The meaning depends on how the word is used.

For example, the word *pupil* can mean two different things.

I am a *pupil* at the Bowen Elementary School.

The *pupil* is the black, center part of your eye.

Use the homographs in the box to answer the following questions.

story	swallow	hide	lock

1. What is the outer skin of an elephant? _____

2. What do you do when you fasten something tightly? _____

3. What do you do after you chew your food? _____

4. What is a fairy tale or folk tale? _____

5. What do you do if you don't want someone to find you? _____

6. What is a curl of hair? _____

7. What is the name of a small bird? _____

8. What is a floor in an apartment building? _____

© Macmillan/McGraw-Hill

CA R 1.4 Use knowledge of antonyms, synonyms, homophones, and homographs to determine the meanings of words.

Name _____

Using the Word Study Steps

1. LOOK at the word.

2. SAY the word aloud.

3. STUDY the letters in the word.

4. WRITE the word.

5. CHECK the word.
   Did you spell the word right?
   If not, go back to step 1.

Find Rhyming Words

Circle the word in each row that rhymes with the spelling word on the left.

1. **unfair**	before	prepare	unpaid
2. **misread**	seed	played	sad
3. **recall**	tail	tell	shawl
4. **presale**	e-mail	unpaid	misdate
5. **unload**	roast	stole	road
6. **mistreat**	complete	displease	mistake
7. **preplan**	prepay	mailman	retail
8. **misfile**	tile	white	fill
9. **retold**	restore	unload	unsold
10. **unwanted**	painted	haunted	planted
11. **precut**	root	rut	cub
12. **undone**	run	dome	drawn
13. **recycle**	refill	bicycle	Michael
14. **misnumber**	timber	lumber	bomber
15. **unhappy**	sloppy	sappy	droopy

© Macmillan/McGraw-Hill

LC 1.8 Spell correctly one-syllable words that have blends, contractions, compounds, orthographic patterns (e.g., *qu*, consonant doubling, changing the ending of a word from *-y* to *-ies* when forming the plural), and common homophones (e.g., *hair-hare*).

Name _____

Practice

Spelling:
Words with
Prefixes *re-*, *un-*,
pre-, *mis-*

Proofreading

A. There are six spelling mistakes in the e-mail message below. Circle the misspelled words. Write the words correctly on the lines below.

Hi Patrick,

My family is at the beach for a week. We brought so much stuff that it took hours to unlod the car! Do you recal the pictures of the house we stayed in last year? I'm sending you a picture of the one we're staying in this year. I love it because it's right on the beach. The beach is really uncrowded this year, too, so we have lots of room to play. My mom and dad preplanned everything before we left for the beach. They packed kites and boogie boards for nice days. They also brought games so we won't be unhapy if it rains.

I am going to help out with a wildlife protection group while I'm here. We're going to make signs to remind people not to misstreat the seagulls and other birds. I think it's unfaire when people chase them or throw things at them. We're also going to recycal trash we find on the beach.

Write back. Then I'll send you more pictures of me at the beach.

                Your friend,

                Sam

1. _____   3. _____   5. _____

2. _____   4. _____   6. _____

Writing Activity

B. Write an e-mail message to a friend about something you have done with a family member or friend. Use at least four spelling words.

_____

_____

_____

© Macmillan/McGraw-Hill

LC 1.8 Spell correctly one-syllable words that have blends, contractions, compounds, orthographic patterns (e.g., *qu*, consonant doubling, changing the ending of a word from -*y* to -*ies* when forming the plural), and common homophones (e.g., *hair-hare*).

Name _____

- A verb in the **past tense** tells about an action that already happened.
- Add **-ed** to most verbs to show past tense.
- If a verb ends with **e,** drop the **e** and add **-ed** to show past tense.
- If a verb ends with a consonant and **y,** change **y** to **i** and add **-ed.**
- If a verb ends with one vowel and one consonant, double the consonant and add **-ed.**

Choose the correct past-tense verb for each sentence. Circle your answer.

1. Felix _____ across the beach.   marchedd   marched

2. The hot sand _____ his feet.   burnd   burned

3. The sand dunes _____ toward the water.   sloped   slopped

4. Felix _____ down the dunes.   rolld   rolled

5. He _____ the sand off his face.   dusted   dustted

6. Casey _____ from the water.   wavved   waved

7. Felix _____ toward the water.   skippd   skipped

8. The waves _____ over his feet.   splashd   splashed

9. Felix _____ on his back.   floated   floatted

10. Casey _____ to do a handstand.   tryed   tried

11. Jellyfish _____ on the water.   coasted   coastted

12. We _____ in the shade.   ressted   rested

LC 1.3 Identify and use **past**, present, and future verb tenses properly in writing and speaking.

Name _____

- A verb in the **past tense** tells about an action that already happened.
- Add **-ed** to most verbs to show past tense.
- If a verb ends with **e,** drop the **e** and add **-ed** to show past tense.
- If a verb ends with a consonant and **y,** change **y** to **i** and add **-ed.**
- If a verb ends with one vowel and one consonant, double the consonant and add **-ed.**

A. Proofread the paragraph. Circle past-tense verbs that are incorrect.

On Saturday, our class clean up the beach at Perch Bay. We picked up litter twigs and seaweed. We packked the other garbage into bags. We discoverred all kinds of things while we work. Sam showd me movie tickets bottle tops and even a watch. The beach lookked much better when we were finished. The sand glitterd like the sun on the water. I'm glad we workd so hard at the beach.

B. Rewrite the paragraph. Write the past-tense verbs correctly. Add commas where necessary.

_____
_____
_____
_____
_____
_____

© Macmillan/McGraw-Hill

CA **LC 1.3** Identify and use **past**, present, and future verb tenses properly in writing and speaking.

Name _____

Writing Rubric

4 Excellent	3 Good	2 Fair	1 Unsatisfactory
Ideas and Content/ Genre	Ideas and Content/ Genre	Ideas and Content/ Genre	Ideas and Content/ Genre
Organization and Focus	Organization and Focus	Organization and Focus	Organization and Focus
Sentence Structure/ Fluency	Sentence Structure/ Fluency	Sentence Structure/ Fluency	Sentence Structure/ Fluency
Conventions	Conventions	Conventions	Conventions
Word Choice	Word Choice	Word Choice	Word Choice
Voice	Voice	Voice	Voice
Presentation	Presentation	Presentation	Presentation

Follow the directions for changing letters in each word. Write the new word in the blank column.

	Original Word	Subtract and add	New Word	New Word's Meaning
1.	royal	drop the *r*, add *l*		faithful to someone or something
2.	boy	drop the *b*, add *j*		a feeling of happiness or excitement
3.	foil	drop the *f*, add *t*		hard work or labor
4.	voice	drop the *v*, add *ch*		a decision or selection
5.	noise	drop the *n*, add *p*		balance or gracefulness
6.	employ	drop the *empl*, add *ann*		bother or upset someone
7.	coin	drop the *n*, add *l*		wind in rings or spirals
8.	point	drop the *p*, add *j*		place where two parts meet
9.	soil	add a *p* after the *s*		ruin or go bad
10.	toy	drop the *t*, add *all*		a mixture of two or more metals
11.	moist	drop the *m*, add *h*		to lift something up in the air
12.	destroy	drop the *destr*, add *ster* to the end of the word		ocean mollusk that lives in shells

© Macmillan/McGraw-Hill

CA **R 1.1** Know and use complex word families when reading (e.g., *-ight*) to decode unfamiliar words.

Name _____

A. Read the story. Then fill in the blanks with the correct words from the box.

instance   illustrate   style   textures   sketches   suggestions

From the time she was a child, Jenna knew she wanted to

_____ children's books. Jenna had her own

_____ of drawing. It was different from that of any

artist she had ever seen. Her _____ had something

special in them. For _____, Jenna always drew a piece

of hair sticking up from the heads of all of her characters.

Jenna loved to paint with oil paints. Some of her paintings had smooth

_____. In others, the paint was thick and rough.

As she grew up, Jenna took several classes in drawing and painting.

_____ from her teachers helped Jenna improve her

work. When Jenna finished the pictures for her first children's book, she

thanked all the teachers who had helped her along the way.

B. Using the clues in the story, write the definitions of these vocabulary words. Check your definitions with a dictionary.

1. instance _____

2. illustrate _____

3. style _____

4. textures _____

© Macmillan/McGraw-Hill

CA R 1.0 Word Analysis, Fluency, and Systematic Vocabulary Development

Name _____

In a story, events take place in a certain **sequence**, or chronological order.

Read the events. For each event, write what you think might happen next. Use clue words, such as *first*, *next*, *then*, and *finally*.

1. Bryan went to the art store.

_____

_____

2. The end of Natasha's pencil broke.

_____

_____

3. Naomi finished sketching the tree on her paper.

_____

_____

4. Bryan took out his sketch pad and reached for his pencil box.

_____

_____

5. Naomi painted the last few details on her painting.

_____

_____

Name _____

As you read *What Do Illustrators Do?*, fill in the Sequence Chart.

┌─────────────────────────────────────┐
│   **Event**   │
└─────────────────────────────────────┘
                  ↓
┌─────────────────────────────────────┐
│   **Event**   │
└─────────────────────────────────────┘
                  ↓
┌─────────────────────────────────────┐
│   **Event**   │
└─────────────────────────────────────┘
                  ↓
┌─────────────────────────────────────┐
│   **Event**   │
└─────────────────────────────────────┘
                  ↓
┌─────────────────────────────────────┐
│   **Event**   │
└─────────────────────────────────────┘

How does the information you wrote in this Sequence Chart help you
analyze text structure in *What Do Illustrators Do?*

As I read, I will pay attention to phrasing and pacing.

	Most of us wish we could draw people. Whether you
10	want to illustrate a story or design a poster, the ability to
22	draw people comes in handy.
27	We all look at faces every day. But beginning artists
37	still have trouble putting what they see on paper. For
47	instance, they often draw the eyes too low. They make
57	the top of the head too small. The people they draw look
69	like pinheads!
71	You don't need special supplies to learn to draw. All
81	you really need to get started is an ordinary pencil and a
93	good eraser. Use any kind of plain white paper.
102	It's a good idea to start by copying other drawings
112	and photographs. You will get better with practice.
120	Then you can surprise your friends and family by
129	drawing them. 131

Comprehension Check

1. What are some common mistakes for beginning artists? **Main Idea and Details**

2. What is a way to become a better artist? **Main Idea and Details**

	Words Read	–	Number of Errors	=	Words Correct Score
First Read		–		=	
Second Read		–		=	

© Macmillan/McGraw-Hill

CA **R 1.3** Read aloud narrative and expository text fluently and accurately and with appropriate **pacing**, intonation, and expression.

Name _____

An **interview** is a written record of a conversation in which the interviewer asks someone questions in order to gather information.

Read the interview. Then answer the questions.

Interviewer: When did you open your art school?

Cora Amble: I opened the art school last year. At first, I worked with students I knew from being an art teacher at their school.

Interviewer: What kind of classes can students take in your school?

Cora Amble: They can take classes in watercolor, oil paint, pastels, or pottery. Also, they can learn to make pots, mugs, or animal figures out of clay.

Interviewer: Do you have many students in your school?

Cora Amble: Twenty-five students are enrolled right now. I would like to hire another teacher so I can take more students.

1. What does Cora Amble do for a living?

_____

2. When did Cora's art school first open?

_____

3. What kind of art do Cora's students learn?

_____

_____

4. Why does Cora want to hire another art teacher?

_____

© Macmillan/McGraw-Hill

CA **R 2.1** Use titles, tables of contents, chapter headings, glossaries, and indexes to locate information in text.

Sentence clues are other words in the same or a nearby sentence that come before or after an unfamiliar word. Sentence clues can help you figure out the meaning of a word.

Circle the context clues that help you figure out the meaning of the underlined word in each sentence. Write a possible definition of the word.

1. The artist looked at the <u>barren</u> canvas and filled the blank space with drawings of bright flowers.

   barren: _____

2. Illustrators need to <u>consider</u> all the scenes in a story as they think about what pictures to draw.

   consider: _____

3. The famous painting was <u>obscured</u> by the large crowd standing in front of it.

   obscured: _____

4. The <u>sketches</u> an illustrator makes at first are quick and rough drawings.

   sketches: _____

5. Some illustrators <u>excel</u> at drawing faces, but others cannot draw faces very well.

   excel: _____

6. The artist makes <u>outlines</u> or sketches the shapes of what will go on the pages of his book before he paints them.

   outlines: _____

© Macmillan/McGraw-Hill

R 1.6 Use sentence and word context to find the meaning of unknown words.

Using the Word Study Steps

1. LOOK at the word.

2. SAY the word aloud.

3. STUDY the letters in the word.

4. WRITE the word.

5. CHECK the word.
Did you spell the word right?
If not, go back to step 1.

Find Rhyming Words

Circle the word in each row that rhymes with the word in dark type.

1. royal	roll	loyal	lowly
2. toil	foil	flow	fool
3. voice	choose	choice	chore
4. spoiled	older	bold	boiled
5. toys	tools	toes	enjoys
6. joins	count	coins	coy
7. boil	soil	sore	sold
8. joint	paint	pond	point
9. boys	noise	nose	noisy
10. awful	joyful	soybean	joke

© Macmillan/McGraw-Hill

LC 1.8 Spell correctly one-syllable words that have blends, contractions, compounds, orthographic patterns (e.g., *qu*, consonant doubling, changing the ending of a word from -y to ies when forming the plural), and common homophones (e.g., *hair-hare*).

What Do Illustrators Do?
Grade 3/Unit 3 **175**

A. There are six spelling mistakes in the letter below. Circle the misspelled words. Write the words correctly on the lines below.

Dear Ms. Jones,

I am a loual fan of your work as an illustrator. I wanted to ask you about what it takes to do your job because I want to be an illustrator, too. Everyone says I draw well, so it seems like a good choys for me.

Your drawings make so many people joieful. I wish I could do that! Even my Uncle Bob, who never smiles, engues your drawings.

When did you decide to become an illustrator? What do you do every day? Is it hard? Are there times when you toyel over a drawing for a long time?

I think the best job for me would be one that I love. My poynt is that I think I would be a good illustrator. Thanks for being my hero!

Sincerely,
Albert Martin

1. _____   4. _____

2. _____   5. _____

3. _____   6. _____

B. Writing Activity

Think about a hero you have and write a letter about why you look up to him or her. Use at least three spelling words in your letter.

_____

_____

_____

_____

LC 1.8 Spell correctly one-syllable words that have blends, contractions, compounds, orthographic patterns (e.g., *qu*, consonant doubling, changing the ending of a word from -y to ies when forming the plural), and common homophones (e.g., *hair-hare*).

© Macmillan/McGraw-Hill

Name _____

- A **present-tense verb** tells what happens now.
- A **past-tense verb** tells about an action that already happened.
- A verb in the **future tense** tells about an action that is going to happen.
- To write about the future, use the special verb *will*.

Each sentence below has a time clue that tells whether the action is happening now, in the past, or in the future. Choose the correct form of the verb to complete each sentence. Write your answer on the line.

1. Now Pete (needs, needed) a gift for his Uncle Carl. _____

2. Tomorrow he (will shop, shop) for something. _____

3. Years ago, Uncle Carl (will play, played) baseball. _____

4. Today he (works, worked) as an announcer at games.

   _____

5. Now Pete (walks, walked) through the stores. _____

6. In the past, his mother (will pick, picked) out presents for him.

   _____

7. Now he (chooses, will choose) a big book about baseball.

   _____

8. The baseball teams in the book (play, played) many years ago.

   _____

9. Pete (will give, gives) it to Uncle Carl on Saturday. _____

10. Uncle Carl (enjoyed, will enjoy) reading the book on the plane ride

    home. _____

LC 1.3 Identify and use past, present, and **future** verb tenses properly in writing and speaking.

What Do Illustrators Do?
Grade 3/Unit 3
177

Name _____

- A **present-tense verb** tells what happens now.
- A **past-tense verb** tells about an action that already happened.
- A **future-tense verb** tells about an action that is going to happen.

A. Read the dialogue. Circle any verbs that are not written in the correct tense or do not agree with their subjects.

"Ann I hoped you can help me, said Jim.

I will tried my best, said Ann.

I needs a gift for Aunt Cara, said Jim.

She will mention something last week, said Ann.

Tell me now! cry Jim.

She said that next year she will learned to fly, said Ann.

"I will looked for a book about airplanes, said Jim.

"That's great Jim! I think she will liked that," said Ann.

B. Writing Activity

Rewrite the dialogue. Write verbs correctly. Make sure that quotation marks are in the right place. Be sure to put a comma before the name of anyone being spoken to.

_____

_____

_____

_____

_____

_____

_____

CA **LC 1.3** Identify and use past, present, and **future** verb tenses properly in writing and speaking.

Name _____

Recess
By: Josie Fredricks

　　　Our walk broke into a run as we sprang onto the playground for recess.
I plugged my ears as I ran by the screaming kids arguing over who would
go first on the monkey bars. I leaped over puddles of water from last
night's rain. It smelled like rain. The grass was as green as the broccoli
I ate last night! I sat down on the damp grass to eat my snack before the
kickball game began. My tongue turned red with the strawberry flavor of
my fruit roll-up.

1. Read the journal entry above:

2. Please look at the chart below. Each of your 5 senses is listed across the
top, and under each heading is a sensory detail from the journal entry
above that goes along with each sense.

Setting: Playground

Sound	Smell	Sight	Touch	Taste
Screaming	Rain	Puddles, green grass	Damp grass	Strawberry roll-up

3. Using the charts below, try to think of sensory details that you might be
able to write about to describe the settings listed. Remember, sensory
details are descriptions of sight, taste, touch, hearing, and smell.

Setting: Cafeteria

Sound	Smell	Sight	Touch	Taste

Setting: In a kitchen, making pizza dough

Sound	Smell	Sight	Touch	Taste

4. Now try it with a setting of your choice.

Name _____

Circle the words in the boxes below that have the same vowel sounds as in the examples.

/ü/ (**oo**, **ue**, **ew**) as in **pool, duel, or new**

chew	hood	cruel	boost
foot	mood	stood	stoop

/ŭ/ (**oo**) as in **wood** or **cook**

goose	shook	boom	wool
good	smooth	flood	hoof

/ü/ (**oo**, **ue**, **ew**, **u_e**) pool, duel, new, rude

drew	look	news	foot
flute	broom	cooking	sue

CA **R 1.1** Know and use complex word families when reading (e.g., -*ight*) to decode unfamiliar words.

© Macmillan/McGraw-Hill

Name _____

A. Choose a word from the box to complete each sentence below.

annual	potential	politely
expensive	innocent	wrapping

1. This year we changed the place for our _____ family picnic.

2. Use this paper for _____ the big presents.

3. My sister thinks that I broke her suitcase, but I am _____.

4. You should speak _____ to everyone, not just adults.

5. The airplane tickets were so _____ that we took the bus instead.

6. The spaceship journey may be dangerous, but it has great

   _____ for new information about Mars.

B. Write a sentence using the vocabulary words correctly.

7. annual _____

   _____

8. expensive _____

   _____

Sometimes readers need to infer, or figure out, what is happening in a story from clues that the author gives. To **make inferences**, add what you know to what the author tells you.

Read the paragraph and answer the questions.

Last year my brothers, my mom, and I took a trip to Chicago. Dad stayed home. This year we're planning a trip to New York City. Dad is making up our sightseeing schedule again. We always follow his advice and have a great time. I like to call him every day and tell him what we did. Dad says he doesn't have to leave home to travel to cities in the United States because they are as close as his travel magazines and books. Next year we may even go to Mexico.

1. How does Dad feel about his family taking trips without him?

_____

2. Explain how you know. _____

_____

_____

3. Do you think Dad will travel with his family to Mexico? Why or why not?

_____

_____

4. Do you think the narrator would like Dad to travel with the family? Why or

why not? _____

_____

CA R 2.0 Reading Comprehension

As you read *The Jones Family Express*, fill in the
Inference Chart.

Clues	Inference

How does the information you wrote in this Inference Chart help you
visualize details in *The Jones Family Express*?

© Macmillan/McGraw-Hill

Name _____

As I read, I will pay attention to intonation and expression.

	"How are you two doing?" the conductor asked Marie.
9	"Fine, thanks," Marie said **politely**.
14	Marie then asked her dad, "How's Rosie?" She was
23	talking about her tiny black poodle. Her mom was holding
33	the tiny dog in a baby carrier around her neck.
43	"She's just fine," Mr. Diaz told her. "Rosie is sleeping."
53	Her parents wanted to leave Rosie home, but Marie
62	insisted that her new puppy was too young to leave behind.
73	She was so small she'd be no trouble at all. Her parents
85	finally agreed.
87	Marie spent the last hours of the trip reading. Her new
98	book was so interesting that it made the hours pass quickly.
109	Soon she felt the train slow down. Her heart began to
120	beat fast. 122

Comprehension Check

1. How did Marie convince her parents to bring Rosie on their trip? **Plot Development**

2. Why did Marie's heart begin to beat faster? **Plot Development**

	Words Read	–	Number of Errors	=	Words Correct Score
First Read		–		=	
Second Read		–		=	

© Macmillan/McGraw-Hill

 R 1.3 Read aloud narrative and expository text fluently and accurately and with appropriate pacing, **intonation**, and **expression**.

Name _____

Reading **directions** often involves following steps that tell you what to do. The steps are numbered because that is the order they are to be followed in. Begin with the first step, number 1, and continue in order through all the remaining steps.

Read the paragraph and the directions. Then answer the questions that follow.

Carlos and some friends plan to take the bus to Zoo Land Amusement Park. They called the local bus company for directions. They got the following information:

1. Catch the #4 crosstown bus on the corner of Elm and Spruce. You need exact change for the fare. The fare is 50 cents for students under 18 and $1.00 for adults. Get a transfer.
2. Ride the #4 crosstown bus to the corner of State and Main. It is about a ten-block bus ride.
3. At State Street, transfer to the #7 downtown bus. You do not need to pay again.
4. Ride the #7 bus to the last bus stop.
5. When you leave the bus, you will see the entrance sign, "Zoo Land Amusement Park."
6. Have fun!

1. How will Carlos and his friends get to the amusement park? _____

2. What transportation will they take first? _____

3. How much will it cost them? _____

4. Where will Carlos and his friends transfer buses? _____

5. Where will they ride the #7 bus to? _____

© Macmillan/McGraw-Hill

CA **R 2.1** Use titles, tables of contents, chapter headings, glossaries, and indexes to locate information in text.

The Jones Family Express 185
Grade 3/Unit 3

Name _____

> **Homophones** are words that sound alike but are spelled differently have different meanings.

A. Circle the correct word to complete each sentence.

1. We brushed the horse's (main, mane) before the show.

2. I used butter, (flour, flower), and sugar to make the cookies.

3. Dad and I need to tighten the (break, brake) on my bike.

4. We need more wind to (sail, sale) the boat.

5. There was a (wrap, rap) on the window.

6. What is the name of the (mane, main) street near your house?

7. I picked this beautiful red (flower, flour) for my aunt.

8. Tasha dropped the glass, but it did not (brake, break).

9. Mom and I went to the back-to-school (sale, sail) to buy jeans and t-shirts.

10. I had to (rap, wrap) the present before we left for the party.

B. Write a homophone one the line for each word below.

Example: rows _____rose_____

11. knot _____   16. be _____

12. haul _____   17. deer _____

13. tacks _____   18. steal _____

14. flea _____   19. affect _____

15. scene _____   20. hoarse _____

© Macmillan/McGraw-Hill

CA R 1.4 Use knowledge of antonyms, synonyms, **homophones**, and homographs to determine the meanings of words.

Name _____

blue	gloom	loop	shook
clue	goose	mules	spoon
cubes	look	shoe	true

Crossword Puzzle

Solve the crossword puzzle with spelling words that complete the sentences.

ACROSS

1. The story about the elephant going on vacation was _____.

2. We stacked the _____ to show the math problem.

4. Did you _____ at Tina's pictures from her family vacation?

5. I can't find the black _____ that my aunt wants to wear.

6. The _____ at that pond is the biggest I've ever seen.

7. The _____ worked hard carrying loads of hay on the farm.

DOWN

2. Can you give me a _____ about what to get my aunt for her birthday?

3. Do you think she would like a new _____ for a gift?

4. The big red _____ looked pretty tied around the gift.

5. The building _____ as the train roared past.

6. The store was dark and gave a sense of _____.

7. The sky was perfectly clear and bright _____.

© Macmillan/McGraw-Hill

LC 1.8 Spell correctly one-syllable words that have blends, contractions, compounds, orthographic patterns (e.g., *qu*, consonant doubling, changing the ending of a word from -y to -ies when forming the plural), and common homophones (e.g., *hair-hare*).

The Jones Family Express
Grade 3/Unit 3

187

A. There are six spelling mistakes in the travel brochure below. Circle the misspelled words. Write the words correctly on the lines below.

A family camping trip is a wonderful way to spend time together and get away from it all. You might want to louk into going in the spring. The bloo skies and green trees will be a nice change from the classroom and the office.

There is a lot to do while camping. You can go for a bike ride or take a hike on a trail. Go on a nature walk. You might see a deer or a gousse.

Cooking on a camping trip is also a lot of fun. Bring a pot, a wooden spoune, and some vegetables to make stue on the campfire. Do not forget to pack some snacks, too! It's tru that you won't have all of the comforts of home, but that makes the camping trip even more special!

1. _____
2. _____
3. _____
4. _____
5. _____
6. _____

B. Writing Activity

Write a postcard to a friend about a journey you have taken or would like to take. Use at least four spelling words in your description.

_____

_____

_____

_____

_____

CA **LC 1.8** Spell correctly one-syllable words that have blends, contractions, compounds, orthographic patterns (e.g., *qu*, consonant doubling, changing the ending of a word from -y to -ies when forming the plural), and common homophones (e.g., *hair-hare*).

Name _____

> • Two sentences can be combined by joining the predicates with *and*.
>
> Two sentences: Jan draws with pencils.
>   Jan sculpts with clay.
>
> Combined sentence: Jan draws with pencils and sculpts
>   with clay.

**Underline the predicates in each pair of sentences. Combine the
two sentences, and write your combined sentence on the line.**

1. Elaine goes to art school. Elaine studies painting.

_____

2. The students sketch outside. The students paint in the classroom.

_____

3. Elaine mixes paint. Elaine invents colors.

_____

4. The brush sweeps the canvas. The brush leaves colors behind.

_____

5. The students look at paintings. The students talk about them.

_____

6. Elaine stands near the tree. Elaine draws the bird.

_____

7. The teacher points to a painting. The teacher explains it.

_____

8. Elaine finishes her painting. Elaine shows it to others.

_____

© Macmillan/McGraw-Hill

A. Proofread the paragraph. Find and underline the pairs of sentences that share the same subject and can be combined.

My mom is an illustrator. She draws pictures for books. She paints pictures for books. I like to watch her work. She reads the book. She takes notes. Sometimes I read it, too. We talk about the characters. We think about how they look. Then Mom makes some sketches. She experiments. She tests out ideas. She decides what belongs on each page. Then she is ready to paint.

Mom decides on colors. Mom mixes the paint. Then she stands at her easel. We talk while she paints. Her brush moves fast. Her brush fills the canvas with color. The shapes grow. The shapes turn into a picture. The finished picture is beautiful.

B. Rewrite the paragraph with the combined sentences.

_____

_____

_____

_____

_____

_____

_____

_____

_____

_____

© Macmillan/McGraw-Hill

CA LC 1.0 Written and Oral English Language Conventions

Name _____

1. Read the sentence below:

   Jamie led us on a barefoot walk through the woods.

2. Now write 3 sentences using sensory details that show what the walk was like.

   Example: The forest smelled like a pile of wet leaves. Sometimes soft moss tickled the bottoms of my feet and other times my toes squished into slimy mud. Everything was silent except for the sound of the breeze rustling the branches all around us.

   _____

   _____

   _____

   _____

   _____

   _____

   _____

   _____

   _____

   _____

Extra Practice: Try the same exercise again using the following sentence.

   We waded in the shallow water at the ocean's edge.

When two vowel sounds appear together in the same syllable, they are pronounced as one sound. The letters **ou** and **ow** can stand for **/ou/**, the vowel sound you hear in *found* and *crowd*.

Use the words in the box with the /ou/ sound to complete the sentences.

bow	shout	bounce	scout	scowl	round
doubt	towel	found	sound	proud	ground

1. The ball took a bad _____ and got past me.

2. Please do not _____ in the library, because many people are studying and reading.

3. The cast of the play came out and took a _____.

4. I hurt my leg when I slipped on the ice and fell on the hard

   _____.

5. After winning the science contest, I was very _____.

6. When Fiona got to the pool, she found the _____ that she thought she had put in her bag.

7. The _____ of the dog barking outside woke me up.

8. My dad had a _____ on his face when I broke the window.

© Macmillan/McGraw-Hill

CA **R 1.1** Know and use complex word families when reading (e.g., -*ight*) to decode unfamiliar words.

Name _____

A. Use the words below to fill in each blank in the story.

argued   beamed   fabric   quarreling   possessions   purchased

One rainy day, Juan and Maria _____ about what to do.

"Let's look through our _____ to see what we don't need.

We can give away toys we do not play with," said Juan.

Their mother _____ at his idea. "I am glad that you

are not greedy children!" she said. This is a much better way to spend time

than _____. A long time ago I _____ a lot

of _____ to make a dress, and I never used it. Take it and

bring it with you. Maybe some children can make costumes with it."

B. Write a definition for each vocabulary word.

1. argued _____

2. beamed _____

3. fabric _____

4. quarreling _____

5. possessions _____

6. purchased _____

A conclusion is a decision you make after looking at all the information about a specific topic. You can **draw conclusions** by considering the information the author gives you and your own experiences. Drawing conclusions helps you better understand what you read.

Read the information below. On the lines below each story, write a conclusion based on information given.

1. Sam walks into the classroom. There is a sign on the bulletin board that says "Welcome, Sam!" The other students invite Sam to join their activity and to sit at their lunch table.

   Conclusion: _____

2. Neighborhood children walk together to a park, carrying trash bags, rakes, and buckets. Three children work together picking up litter in a park. One child rakes leaves, and another shoves leaves into a trash bag. When they are finished, all the children play in the park.

   Conclusion: _____

   _____

3. Kayla brings her box of games over to Jen, and they open it together. They choose a game from the box and play.

   Conclusion: _____

4. Tyler and Grace wash the dishes, sweep the floor, rake leaves, take out the trash, and take their baby brother out in his stroller.

   Conclusion: _____

CA R 2.0 Reading Comprehension

Name _____

As you read *Seven Spools of Thread*, fill in the Conclusion Map.

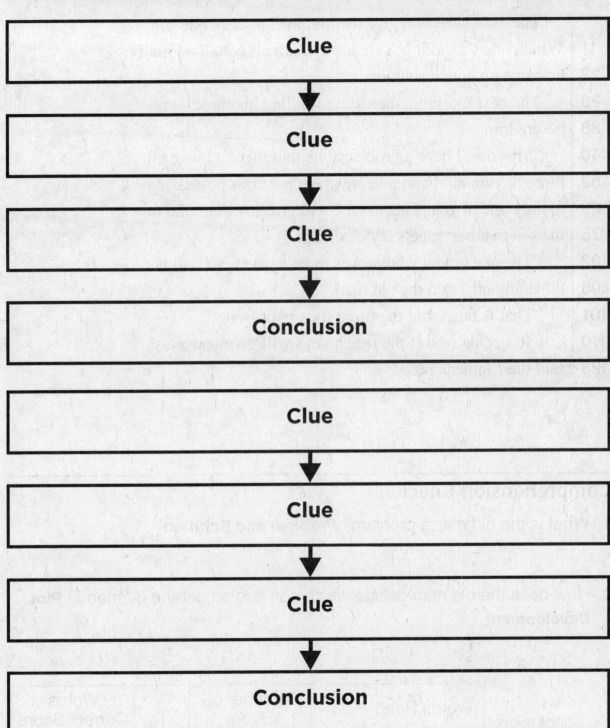

Clue

Clue

Clue

Conclusion

Clue

Clue

Clue

Conclusion

How does the information you wrote in this Conclusion Map help you better understand *Seven Spools of Thread*?

Name _____

As I read, I will pay attention to phrasing.

	The old man could give the diamond to only one son.
11	Which one should it be? He loved them all equally. Finally
22	he came up with a solution.
28	The next morning, the old man called his three sons
38	before him.
40	"My sons, I have a problem," he told them. "I love all
52	three of you, but I can give my most precious possession
63	to only one of you. Therefore, I will give my diamond to
75	the son that best meets my challenge."
82	"The one of you who proves to be a true hero will get
95	the diamond," said the old man.
101	"That is fair," said the three sons in unison.
110	"To decide who is the true hero, I will give you a task,"
123	said their father. 126

Comprehension Check

1. What is the old man's problem? **Problem and Solution**

2. How does the old man decide which son should get the diamond? **Plot Development**

	Words Read	−	Number of Errors	=	Words Correct Score
First Read		−		=	
Second Read		−		=	

© Macmillan/McGraw-Hill

CA **R 1.3** Read aloud narrative and expository text fluently and accurately and with appropriate pacing, intonation, and expression.

Name _____

> **Rules** are directions or guides that help people to act properly in different situations. There are rules for behaving in school. Games have rules to play by, and clubs have rules for members to follow.

Answer the questions below.

1. Why are rules important?

_____

_____

2. Name one place where rules are important and tell why.

_____

_____

3. What are some rules in your classroom?

_____

_____

4. What are some rules that you have in your home?

_____

_____

R 2.1 Use titles, tables of contents, chapter headings, glossaries, and indexes to locate information in text.

Some words have more than one meaning. Use a dictionary to find two meanings for each word below and write each meaning under the word.

1. stick

Definition 1: _____

Definition 2: _____

2. corner

Definition 1: _____

Definition 2: _____

3. row

Definition 1: _____

Definition 2: _____

4. raise

Definition 1: _____

Definition 2: _____

5. block

Definition 1: _____

Definition 2: _____

6. Write a sentence that uses both meanings of one of the words above. Your sentence should tell something about getting along with others.

_____

_____

_____

© Macmillan/McGraw-Hill

CA **R 1.0** Word Analysis, Fluency, and Systematic Vocabulary Development

Using the Word Study Steps

1. LOOK at the word.

2. SAY the word aloud.

3. STUDY the letters in the word.

4. WRITE the word.

5. CHECK the word.
   Did you spell the word right?
   If not, go back to step 1.

Find Rhyming Words

Circle the word in each row that rhymes with the word in dark type.

1. **towel**	sole	owl	bowl
2. **ouch**	couch	foul	loud
3. **sound**	sew	down	ground
4. **out**	shout	mound	town
5. **frown**	own	town	snow
6. **found**	out	scout	round
7. **ounce**	bounce	howl	once
8. **bow**	plow	plot	hope
9. **cloud**	proud	clock	draw
10. **shout**	snow	scout	stop
11. **loud**	crowd	long	couch
12. **bow**	louder	clouds	plow

LC 1.8 Spell correctly one-syllable words that have blends,
contractions, compounds, orthographic patterns (e.g., *qu*, consonant
doubling, changing the ending of a word from -y to -ies when forming
the plural), and common homophones (e.g., *hair-hare*).

Seven Spools of Thread
Grade 3/Unit 4
199

Proofreading

A. There are six spelling mistakes in this paragraph. Circle the misspelled words. Write the words correctly on the lines below.

Our Class Newsletter

Our class is prowd to announce that we have come up with some new rules. The lunchroom has gotten looder over the past year. We fownd it is hard to enjoy eating our lunches. As a group we have decided that to fix the problem we will do two things. First, everyone must sit at one of the rond tables during lunch. There must be no walking around. Second, you are not allowed to schot at each other or stomp on the growned. These new rules should make lunchtime much better. If we make the lunchroom a nicer place, everyone will want to eat there.

1. _____   4. _____

2. _____   5. _____

3. _____   6. _____

Writing Activity

B. Write an article for your class newsletter. Use at least three spelling words in your paragraph.

_____

_____

_____

_____

_____

LC 1.8 Spell correctly one-syllable words that have blends, contractions, compounds, orthographic patterns (e.g., *qu*, consonant doubling, changing the ending of a word from -y to -ies when forming the plural), and common homophones (e.g., *hair-hare*).

© Macmillan/McGraw-Hill.

- The verb **be** has special forms. The chart shows which form of *be* to use with a sentence subject.

SUBJECT	PRESENT	PAST
he, she, it	**is**	**was**
we, you, they	**are**	**were**
I	**am**	**was**

Write the correct form of *be* to finish each sentence.

1. Tanya _____ a baker.

2. She _____ 16 years old when she took her first baking job.

3. We _____ among her first customers at her shop.

4. We _____ nearby when the shop opened.

5. Now we _____ big fans of her strawberry pies.

6. They _____ the best pies in the world.

7. I _____ certain you would like them.

8. Years ago, Tanya _____ a strawberry picker.

9. "That is why I _____ now a strawberry expert," she explains.

10. Strawberries _____ at their best in June.

11. Baking _____ lots of fun!

12. Where _____ the sugar for the strawberries?

13. Tanya _____ mixing the batter.

14. We _____ ready to put the pie in the oven.

© Macmillan/McGraw-Hill

CA **LC 1.4** Identify and use subjects and verbs correctly in speaking and writing simple sentences.

Seven Spools of Thread **201**
Grade 3/Unit 4

Name _____

- Remember that the verbs **be**, **do**, and **have** have special forms.

A. Proofread the passage. Circle any incorrect uses of *be*, *do*, or *have*.

I is learning to bake. Grandma are teaching me. We was at her house today. She asked if I knew how to bake a strawberry shortcake. I told her I did not. I does like strawberries, though! Grandma agreed to let me help her.

After we baked the cake, we served it to the family.

"I is very impressed," declared Mom.

"It be a fantastic strawberry shortcake!" said Dad.

"You does a great job!" said Grandma.

"We was a good team," I said.

B. Writing Activity

Rewrite the passage. Use the correct forms of *be*, *do*, or *have*.

_____

_____

_____

_____

_____

_____

_____

_____

_____

CA **LC 1.4** Identify and use subjects and verbs correctly in speaking and writing simple sentences.

Name _____

1. Please read these sentences.

    Jill said that she was going home. Amanda said that she was too.

This second set replaces these "telling" statements with dialogue that give a much clearer picture of what is happening. For example:

    Jill said, "I've had enough of this. I'm going home." "Me too," Amanda agreed. "I've never been so cold in my life."

2. Rewrite these sentences. Try to SHOW how Paul and Jimmy, and then Janet and Michael were feeling by the kind of words that they use.

    a. Paul said that he did not want to finish the game. Jimmy said that he wanted to keep playing.

    b. Janet asked who had the remote control. Michael said that Janet had it last.

_____

_____

_____

_____

_____

_____

_____

_____

Extra Practice: Rewrite these sentences following the above instructions:

    Theo said that he was done with his dinner. Mom said that he wasn't.

The **plural** of many nouns is formed by adding **-s** to the base word, as in *pears*. Nouns ending in **x**, **ch**, and **sh** form the plural by adding **-es**, as in *wishes*.

To form the plural of most nouns that end in a consonant plus *y*, change the **y** to *i* and add **-es**.

Write the plural form of each word. Then use each plural form in a sentence.

rock

1. Plural form _____

_____

branch

2. Plural form _____

_____

bush

3. Plural form _____

_____

country

4. Plural form _____

_____

library

5. Plural form _____

_____

© Macmillan/McGraw-Hill

R 1.1 Know and use complex word families when reading (e.g., *-ight*) to decode unfamiliar words.
R 1.2 Decode regular multisyllabic words.

Name _____

brilliance	affection	pleaded
preparations	guarantee	exhausted

A. Write a complete sentence to answer each question below. In your answer, use the vocabulary word in dark type.

1. When would your class need time for **preparations**?

   _____

2. Why would a soccer player have **pleaded** with the other players on the team?

   _____

3. How might an audience show **affection**?

   _____

4. Why would you want a **guarantee** if you bought a new stereo?

   _____

5. What have you seen that shows **brilliance**?

   _____

6. When would an athlete feel **exhausted**?

   _____

> A **theme** is the message or overall idea that the author wants to tell readers. The theme is not always stated. Sometimes readers need to identify the theme by reading carefully.

Read the passage. Answer the questions that follow.

Jack was having a not-very-good day. First, he fell on the way to school and ripped his jeans. Next, he forgot to bring in his book report. Then he had to go to the dentist after school. When Jack got home, a message was waiting for him. The message was from the school soccer coach, inviting Jack to play goalie on the team. Playing goalie was Jack's dream. For the first time that day, Jack had a big smile on his face.

1. Put a check next to the theme of the passage.

____ Don't rush or you'll have a bad day.

____ A surprise can turn around a bad day.

____ Messages always bring good news.

2. Was the theme stated or unstated? _____

3. What information in the passage helped you decide your answer?

_____

_____

4. Write a short paragraph that has a theme about confidence.

_____

_____

_____

_____

© Macmillan/McGraw-Hill

CA R 3.4 Determine the underlying theme or author's message in fiction and nonfiction text.

Name _____

As you read *Nacho and Lolita*, fill in the Theme Map.

Clue

↓

Clue

↓

Clue

↓

Theme

How does the information you wrote in this Theme Map help you
understand *Nacho and Lolita*?

© Macmillan/McGraw-Hill

R 3.4 Determine the underlying theme or author's message in fiction
and nonfiction text.

Name _____

As I read, I will pay attention to expression.

	A kangaroo rat lives off water in its own body. It also
12	saves water. It builds an underground home or burrow.
21	When the rat breathes, it gives off some water droplets.
31	This water stays inside the burrow.
37	Pack rats store seeds and nuts in their burrows. The
47	seeds and nuts absorb water from the air. This helps pack
58	rats get enough to drink. They chew on a cactus plant only
70	if they are suffering from thirst. Those cactus spines are
80	sharp.
81	Many birds live in the desert. There are owls, hawks,
91	and roadrunners. Desert birds get all their water from the
101	bugs, lizards, and small animals they eat.
108	In the desert sun, water evaporates quickly. To keep
117	cool many desert animals hunt for food at night. 126

Comprehension Check

1. How do pack rats get enough water? **Main Idea and Details**

2. How do birds get their water? **Main Idea and Details**

	Words Read	−	Number of Errors	=	Words Correct Score
First Read		−		=	
Second Read		−		=	

© Macmillan/McGraw-Hill

 R 1.3 Read aloud narrative and expository text fluently and accurately and with appropriate pacing, intonation, and expression.

Consonance is the repetition of the same consonant sound at the end of two or more words.

A **metaphor** is a statement in which one thing is compared to another to suggest a similarity.

A. Choose a word from the word box that shows consonance and completes the sentence. Some words will not be used at all.

hug	floor	mud	eight	gain	den	feel	tone

1. See you tonight. We'll meet at _____.

2. That flower should never be near the _____.

3. The bug and the dog were in a bag and needed a _____.

4. We walked around the flowerbed covered in _____.

B. Tell why each sentence below is an example of a metaphor. Then tell what each sentence means.

5. My friend Denise is a walking dictionary.

_____

_____

6. My flashlight is my shining star.

_____

_____

Related words are words that have similar meanings.
You can use a thesaurus to help you find related words for a
new or unknown word.

This is a thesaurus entry for the word *cease*. The words have
similar meanings, so they are related words.

cease   stop, end, halt, stay, quit

**Find a word from the box that is a related word for the word in
dark print in each sentence. Write the word on the line.**

| sleepy | show | important | hide | part | take |

1. You shouldn't **conceal** your talents.

   Related word _____

2. The artist will **demonstrate** how to draw a dog.

   Related word _____

3. You should **seize** the opportunity to play in the marching band.

   Related word _____

4. I'm trying to memorize my lines, but I keep feeling **drowsy**.

   Related word _____

5. What **portion** of the event would you like to work on?

   Related word _____

6. The coach says today's team meeting is **meaningful**.

   Related word _____

CA **R 1.4** Use knowledge of antonyms, synonyms, homophones, and
homographs to determine the meanings of words.

© Macmillan/McGraw-Hill

Name _____

Using the Word Study Steps

1. LOOK at the word.

2. SAY the word aloud.

3. STUDY the letters in the word.

4. WRITE the word.

5. CHECK the word.
   Did you spell the word right?
   If not, go back to step 1.

X the Word

Put an X on the word in each row that does not fit the pattern.

1.	years	lunches	ash	cherries
2.	cherry	tray	pony	bunches
3.	city	daisies	flies	states
4.	inch	lunches	bunches	cities
5.	state	ponies	ashes	trays
6.	trays	twin	cherries	alleys
7.	fox	ashes	city	munch
8.	daisies	inches	years	fly
9.	twins	foxes	alley	ponies
10.	tray	year	daisy	states
11.	rode	daisies	cherries	ponies
12.	gems	twins	years	space
13.	inches	gems	foxes	boxes
14.	years	flies	cities	ponies

© Macmillan/McGraw-Hill

LC 1.8 Spell correctly one-syllable words that have blends, contractions, compounds, orthographic patterns (e.g., *qu*, consonant doubling, changing the ending of a word from -y to -ies when forming the plural), and common homophones (e.g., *hair-hare*).

Nacho and Lolita • Grade 3/Unit 4 211

Proofreading

A. There are six spelling mistakes in this paragraph. Circle the misspelled words. Write the words correctly on the lines below.

Melody and Melissa were tooins, but they couldn't have been more different. Melody loved picking daisys, arranging flowers, and playing with her stuffed poonys. Melissa loved flis and insects and crawling around in the dirt. The problem was that they shared a room. Melody liked the room to be neat with boonchs of flowers in all the windows. Melissa was far from neat. She tracked in mud and brought bugs into the room. It had been a problem for many years. One day Melody decided that maybe she and Melissa should divide the room in two. That way they could both get what they wanted. Melissa thought it was a great idea. They hung a white sheet a few inshs from the ceiling. Now Melody's room is always beautiful, and Melissa's room is always messy. They are the happiest sisters around.

1. _____   4. _____

2. _____   5. _____

3. _____   6. _____

Writing Activity

B. If you could have your dream room, what would it be like? Use at least three spelling words in your paragraph.

_____

_____

_____

_____

_____

© Macmillan/McGraw-Hill

CA **LC 1.8** Spell correctly one-syllable words that have blends, contractions, compounds, orthographic patterns (e.g., *qu*, consonant doubling, changing the ending of a word from -y to -ies when forming the plural), and common homophones (e.g., *hair-hare*).

> • The verb *be* is a common **linking verb**. *Be* has special forms in the past tense.
>> Jim *was* at the door.
>> My brothers and I *were* sorry.

For each sentence below, write the verb form of *be* that agrees with the subject of the sentence.

1. My brothers and I _____ always fighting.

2. Dad _____ upset about our fights.

3. The solution _____ to make us work together.

4. Our task _____ to build a tree house.

5. We all _____ eager to have a tree house.

6. I _____ in charge of measuring.

7. Dad _____ there to help us cut and nail.

8. We _____ hard at work.

9. It _____ all very peaceful.

10. We _____ glad we did something together.

11. My brothers and I _____ careful with the nails.

12. The wooden planks _____ everywhere.

13. We _____ out back all day.

14. Dad _____ happy with our progress.

15. We _____ thirsty in the hot sun.

LC 1.3 Identify and use past, present, and future verb tenses properly in writing and speaking.

Name _____

- The verb *be* connects the subject to the rest of the sentence.
  Be has special forms in the present tense and the past tense.

PRESENT	PAST
I am	I was
He, she, it is	He, she, it was
They, we are	They, we were

A. Proofread the story. Circle any linking verbs that are not correct.

    my brother and I helped Grandma decorate for Kwanzaa. I is the oldest, so I got the red, black, and green candles. I arranged them in the center of the table

    "That be my job" Carl said. "I did it last year."

    Then we started yelling at each other.

    "Boys" said Grandma. "why don't you work together to arrange the table"

    So we did and made the table look nice. It are not so bad. in fact, we be a pretty good team

B. Rewrite the paragraph. Use the correct linking verbs. Make sure that all sentences begin with a capital letter and have an end mark.

_____

_____

_____

_____

_____

_____

_____

© Macmillan/McGraw-Hill

CA **LC 1.3** Identify and use past, present, and future verb tenses properly in writing and speaking.

1. Please read the following TELLING sentences:

   The turtle escaped. Mom and I were looking for it everywhere.

2. Now turn this into a dialogue. Use verbs that SHOW that the two people were feeling upset.

Example:

I screamed, "The turtle is missing." Then running downstairs, I begged my mother, "Please stop what you are doing and help me look for the turtle until we find it."

_____

_____

_____

_____

_____

3. Rewrite this again, substituting verbs that SHOW that the people are feeling not at all concerned.

_____

_____

_____

_____

_____

Extra Practice: Change the following TELLING sentence into a dialogue using verbs that SHOW that the people are excited:

   Kurt and Myles got ready for Juanita's surprise party.

© Macmillan/McGraw-Hill

Practice

Phonics/Word Study:
Variant Vowels *au*, *aw*,
alt, *alk*, *all*, *ough*

Name _____

The /ô/ sound can be spelled *au*, *aw*, *alt*, *alk*, *all*, and *ough*.

The sound is found in words such as *Paul*, *saw*, *salt*, *walk*, *tall*, and *cough*.

A. Underline the letters that represent the /ô/ sound in each of these words.

1. a u t h o r   6. y a w n e d

2. f a l l e n   7. b r o u g h t

3. c o u g h   8. a u c t i o n

4. b o a r d w a l k   9. s t a l k

5. s t a l l   10. v a u l t

B. Now read the paragraph below. Find and circle four words that have the /ô/ sound. Then continue the story. Circle the words with the /ô/ sound that you use.

    My favorite season is autumn. I love the warm days and cool nights. I like to walk in the fallen leaves. We rake leaves and then jump into the big piles. My dog tries to help us rake by scraping his paws through the leaves.

_____

_____

_____

_____

_____

_____

(CA) **R 1.1** Know and use complex word families when reading (e.g., *-ight*) to decode unfamiliar words.

Name _____

A. Read the story. Then fill in the blanks with the correct words from the box.

utilize	awareness	pollution	emphasize

On the first morning of their vacation, Kate and her dad took a

walk. Kate was excited to find new shells and pieces of beach glass.

Instead, they found all kinds of trash. They were shocked to see the

_____ all over their special beach. Kate's dad wanted

to raise people's _____ about this problem. He decided

to _____ the support of the Parks and Recreation

Department. He also asked Kate to make posters that explained the

problem. He encouraged Kate to _____ that through

teamwork, the community could clean up the trash.

B. Using the clues in the story, write the definitions of these vocabulary words. Check your definitions with a dictionary.

1. utilize _____

2. awareness _____

3. pollution _____

4. emphasize _____

Name _____

Characters in stories often have a difficulty, or **problem**. What the character does to solve the problem is called the **solution**.

Read the passage and answer the questions.

When Dan got his dog at the animal shelter, he learned that the shelter might have to close. There wasn't enough money to pay people, so they needed more volunteers. Dan decided to get his town to help. Dan and his parents organized a pet drive to get donations of pet food, treats, toys, and blankets. Dan started an animal club at school. The club members all agreed to volunteer at the shelter. With the help of others, Dan helped solve an important problem.

1. What is the problem in the story?

_____

_____

2. What does Dan do to solve the problem?

_____

_____

3. Why do you think Dan's efforts to help the shelter were successful?

_____

_____

4. What kind of person do you think Dan is?

_____

_____

_____

CA **R 2.6** Extract appropriate and significant information from the text, including problems and solutions.

Name _____

As you read *A Solution to Pollution*, **fill in the Problem and Solution Chart.**

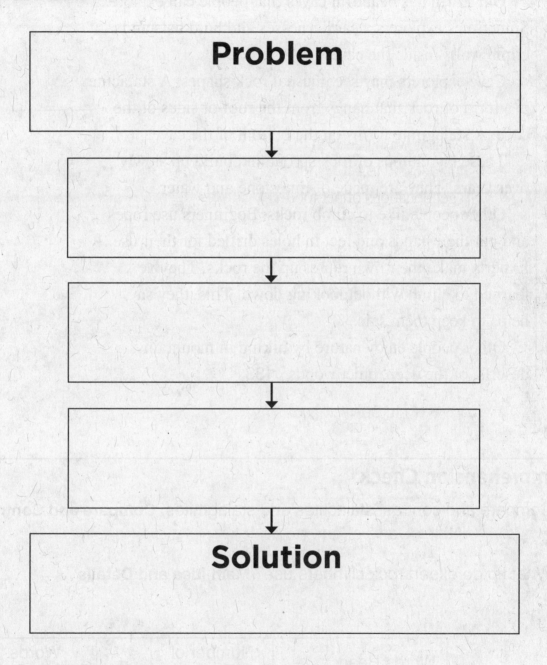

How does the information you wrote in the Problem and Solution Chart help you summarize *A Solution to Pollution*?

© Macmillan/McGraw-Hill

CA **R 2.6** Extract appropriate and significant information from the text, including problems and solutions.

Name _____

As I read, I will pay attention to my pronunciation and phrasing.

	Our Earth has beautiful caves that people can explore.
9	Sometimes explorers wear harnesses and hard hats and
17	climb walls inside the caves.
23	Cave explorers may see unusual rock shapes. A stalactite
32	is a form of rock that hangs from the roof or sides of the
46	cave. A stalagmite forms on the bottom of the cave.
56	These big clumps of rock sprout and build up slowly
66	over years. They are made of limestone and water.
75	Other people like to climb rocks. Beginners use ropes
84	and put their hands and feet in holes drilled for their use.
96	Experts make their own routes up the rocks. They've
105	learned to climb without looking down. This, they say,
114	helps to keep them safe.
119	Other people enjoy nature by hiking in mountains,
127	deserts, or the deep, quiet woods. 133

Comprehension Check

1. Compare and contrast stalactites and stalagmites. **Compare and Contrast**

2. What tip do expert rock climbers use? **Main Idea and Details**

	Words Read	–	Number of Errors	=	Words Correct Score
First Read		–		=	
Second Read		–		=	

© Macmillan/McGraw-Hill

CA **R 1.3** Read aloud narrative and expository text fluently and accurately and with appropriate pacing, intonation, and expression.

Name _____

A **media center** is a place where you can do research. One
way to do research is on a computer using the Internet.
• **Search engine:** a computer program system that looks for
  information on the Internet using key words
• **Key words:** important words that identify a subject
• **URLs:** addresses for where you want to go on the Internet

**A. Choose the URL in the box that would likely have information
about each topic below.**

http://www.farmersmark.org
http://www.healthysummers.com

1. Kinds of programs kids can participate in during the summer months

   URL: _____

2. Where to buy fruits and vegetables from local growers

   URL: _____

B. Answer the questions about key words and search engines.

3. What key words would you type in a search engine to learn about

   protecting the rain forests in South America? _____

   _____

4. What key words would you type in a search engine to learn about

   preventing air pollution? _____

   _____

CA **W 1.3** Understand the structure and organization of various reference
materials (e.g., dictionary, thesaurus, atlas, encyclopedia).

Problem/Solution Writing Frame

A. Summarize *A Solution to Pollution*. **Use the Problem/Solution Writing Frame below.**

California has many beautiful beaches. However, these beaches face several **problems**.

One **problem** is _____ because _____

_____

_____

_____.

Another **problem** is _____ because _____

_____

_____

_____.

To help **solve** these problems, _____

_____

_____

_____.

The **result** is that _____

_____

_____

_____.

B. Rewrite the completed summary on another sheet of paper. Keep it as a model for writing a summary of an article or selection using this text structure.

© Macmillan/McGraw-Hill

CA R 2.0 Reading Comprehension

Suffixes are word parts that can be added to the end of words. Adding a suffix creates a new word with its own meaning. The suffix **-ful** means "full of." The suffix **-ly** means "in a certain manner or way; like."

Read each question below. Add the suffix -ful or -ly to the word in the box that best answers the question. Write the new word on the line after the question. Then write a sentence using the word.

grace	loud	slow	pain	wind	swift	thank

1. How does a broken arm feel? _____

_____

2. How does a deer move? _____

_____

3. How does a turtle move? _____

_____

4. How would you describe a ballet dancer? _____

_____

5. How do fans at a game cheer? _____

_____

6. How do you feel when you receive a gift? _____

_____

R 1.8 Use knowledge of prefixes (e.g., *un-*, *re-*, *pre-*, *bi-*, *mis-*, *dis-*) and suffixes (e.g., *-er*, *-est*, *-ful*) to determine the meaning of words.

A Solution to Pollution
Grade 3/Unit 4   **223**

Name _____

Practice

Spelling:
Words with Variant
Vowels *au*, *aw*, *alt*,
alk, *all*, *ough*

Using the Word Study Steps

1. LOOK at the word.

2. SAY the word aloud.

3. STUDY the letters in the word.

4. WRITE the word.

5. CHECK the word.
Did you spell the word right?
If not, go back to step 1.

X the Word

Put an X on the word in each row that does not fit the pattern.

1.	yawn	lawn	hawks	bought
2.	caused	paused	salt	hauls
3.	drawing	joy	bawls	crawled
4.	crawled	squawk	spoiled	hawks
5.	coins	taught	hauls	caused
6.	bought	salt	halls	falls
7.	drawing	lawn	broom	hawks
8.	paused	stopped	hauls	cause
9.	thought	bought	coughing	spoiled
10.	crawled	bawl	hawk	halls

CA **LC 1.8** Spell correctly one-syllable words that have blends, contractions, compounds, orthographic patterns (e.g., *gu*, consonant doubling, changing the ending of a word from *-y* to *-ies* when forming the plural), and common homophones (e.g., *hair-hare*).

Practice

Spelling:
Words with Variant
Vowels *au*, *aw*, *alt*,
alk, *all*, *ough*

Proofreading

A. There are four spelling mistakes in this list. Circle the misspelled words. Write the words correctly on the lines below.

Steps for making a salad:

1. Always wash your hands with soap and water before you start cooking.

2. Make sure you baught everything you need.

3. Get out the things you will need for the dressing, such as oil, vinegar, and sawlt.

4. Toss together the lettuce and the other vegetables.

5. If you have a garden next to your lown, you can add fresh vegetables to your salad.

6. Remember what you were tought for the next time you make a salad.

1. _____   3. _____

2. _____   4. _____

Writing Activity

B. Write the steps for another activity you like to do. Use at least three spelling words in your paragraph.

_____

_____

_____

_____

_____

_____

_____

LC 1.8 Spell correctly one-syllable words that have blends, contractions, compounds, orthographic patterns (e.g., *qu*, consonant doubling, changing the ending of a word from -*y* to -*ies* when forming the plural), and common homophones (e.g., *hair-hare*).

A Solution to Pollution
Grade 3/Unit 4   **225**

- A **contraction** is a shortened form of two words.
- An **apostrophe** (') shows where one or more letters have been left out. In most contractions with *not*, the apostrophe takes the place of the letter *o*.

Rewrite each sentence using a contraction with *not* in place of the underlined verb. Make the sentence mean the opposite.

1. I <u>did</u> want to share a room with my brothers.

   _____

2. There <u>was</u> enough space for all of us.

   _____

3. There <u>is</u> a place in the house for me to call my own.

   _____

4. At first, we <u>were</u> sure what to do.

   _____

5. "I <u>do</u> mind using the storage room," I told Mom.

   _____

6. "I <u>will</u> mind," said Mom.

   _____

7. I <u>have</u> had a room of my own yet.

   _____

8. I <u>was</u> sure how to fix it up.

   _____

CA LC 1.0 Written and Oral English Language Conventions

Name _____

- A **contraction** is a shortened form of two words.
- An **apostrophe** (') shows where one or more letters have been left out.

A. Proofread these paragraphs. Circle any contractions that are not correctly written.

It's very difficult to share a room. You dont have any space of your own. You cant ever have the whole place to yourself. I had this problem. I shared my room with my brothers. They came in and played when I tried to do homework. We fought all the time. I didnt have a way to get away from everyone!

Then I had an idea. Our attic hadnt been used much. Mom and Dad said that they werent planning to use all the space. I cleared out an area in the attic. I put up curtains to make it private. I found old furniture that wasnt being used. Suddenly I had an office. It's my own special place. Best of all, my brothers and I arent fighting anymore! So if you havent got a place of your own, look around. There might be a special place just waiting for you to find it!

Writing Activity

B. Write a short poem that describes a space of your own. Use at least two contractions.

_____

_____

_____

_____

_____

© Macmillan/McGraw-Hill

Writing Rubric

4 Excellent	3 Good	2 Fair	1 Unsatisfactory
Ideas and Content/ Genre	Ideas and Content/ Genre	Ideas and Content/ Genre	Ideas and Content/ Genre
Organization and Focus	Organization and Focus	Organization and Focus	Organization and Focus
Sentence Structure/ Fluency	Sentence Structure/ Fluency	Sentence Structure/ Fluency	Sentence Structure/ Fluency
Conventions	Conventions	Conventions	Conventions
Word Choice	Word Choice	Word Choice	Word Choice
Voice	Voice	Voice	Voice
Presentation	Presentation	Presentation	Presentation

Name _____

> **Homophones** are words that sound the same but are spelled differently and have different meanings.
> For example, *road*, *rode*, and *rowed* are homophones.

Underline the homophones in each of these sentences. Then write the definition of each homophone.

1. Your donations to our zoo helped so much that you're invited to visit the zoo whenever you wish.

   _____

   _____

2. I need to know where we are going so I can decide what to wear.

   _____

   _____

3. I pretended that I was on the high sea and could see other parts of the world.

   _____

   _____

4. Have you seen the scene in the movie where the kids win the soccer game?

   _____

   _____

R 1.1 Know and use complex word families when reading (e.g., -*ight*) to decode unfamiliar words.

Name _____

A. Read the story. Then fill in each blank with the correct word from the box.

| cross   alarmed   unfortunately   managed   pretend   anxious |

Last month, my family got a new puppy. One day, the puppy dug a hole under the gate. When I went outside to play with him, I was _____ to find that he was gone! I looked around the front yard, but _____ he was nowhere to be seen. I was feeling _____. My dad said, "Don't worry. We'll find him!" My dad _____ the search party. He sent my mom and sister toward the park to search. He sent my brother and his friend into the woods behind our house. He and I headed over toward the creek. I tried to _____ that I wasn't scared, but I was. I thought we'd never see him again! Finally, we spotted him playing in a pile of leaves. He ran up to us when he heard us calling his name. He was so happy to see us that I couldn't be _____ with him. I think he learned his lesson. He hasn't dug a hole since!

B. Using the clues in the story, write the definitions of these vocabulary words. Check your definitions with a dictionary.

1. unfortunately _____

2. pretend _____

3. cross _____

4. alarmed _____

CA R 1.0 Word Analysis, Fluency, and Systematic Vocabulary Development

Name _____

> A story has a **problem** and a **solution**.
> The **problem** in a story is what a character wants to do, needs to find out, or wants to change.
> The way the problem is solved is called the **solution**.

Read the passage and each question. Underline the answer in the passage and then write the answer.

Mrs. Ortiz had to be at work early in the morning. But before she left home she had to walk the dog, make school lunches for Benita and Carlos, and prepare snacks for them to eat when they got home. It was too much for her to do!

One day, she asked Benita and Carlos to join her for a talk. Mrs. Ortiz told them that she had too many things to do before work. She asked them to think of ways to help her. Benita liked to sleep late, but she offered to get up a little earlier so she could walk the dog. Carlos often played ball with his friends after school, but he offered to make snacks before he went off to play. Working together, Benita and Carlos helped Mrs. Ortiz solve her problem.

1. Who has a problem? _____

2. What is the problem? _____

_____

3. What is the first thing Mrs. Ortiz does to solve her problem? _____

_____

4. What do Benita and Carlos do to help her solve her problem? _____

_____

_____

© Macmillan/McGraw-Hill

CA R 2.6 Extract appropriate and significant information from the text, including problems and solutions.

Name _____

As you read *Ramona and Her Father*, fill in the Problem and
Solution Chart.

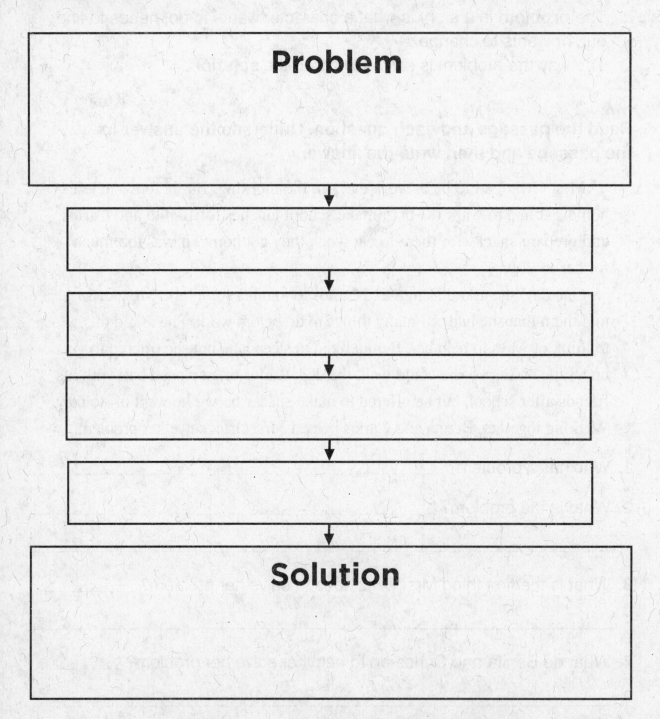

Problem

↓

↓

↓

↓

Solution

How does the information you wrote on the Problem and Solution
Chart help you better understand *Ramona and Her Father*?

CA **R 2.6** Extract appropriate and significant information from the text,
including problems and solutions.

© Macmillan/McGraw-Hill

Name _____

As I read, I will pay attention to intonation.

	One man who came to the United States as a boy helped
12	to save Yosemite's natural wonders for you to enjoy. His
22	name was John Muir.
26	John Muir was born in a small town in Scotland in
37	1838. His family moved to the United States when he was
47	11. They moved to what is now Wisconsin and set up a
58	farm there. They were pioneers.
63	Muir went to school in a small schoolhouse. He liked
73	being a schoolboy. The rest of the time he worked on the
85	farm. He was busy from sunup until sundown. But Muir
95	yearned for more. He knew he didn't want to tend the farm
107	all his life. Muir liked to read, and he read often. He also
120	liked to invent things. He made a special thermometer.
129	And he made something he called his "early-rising
137	machine." 138

Comprehension Check

1. What interests did John Muir have? **Main Idea and Details**

2. What does the word *pioneer* mean? **Context Clues**

	Words Read	−	Number of Errors	=	Words Correct Score
First Read		−		=	
Second Read		−		=	

CA **R 1.3** Read aloud narrative and expository text fluently and accurately and with appropriate pacing, **intonation**, and expression.

In a poem, the **speaker** tells the story and makes the experience more personal.

Alliteration is the repetition of the same beginning sound in a series of words. Tongue twisters use alliteration. "Peter Piper picked a peck of pickled peppers" is an example of alliteration.

A. Complete the alliteration in the following sentences.

1. Barry Barnes bought a big, blue _____.

2. Little Larry Lawson lost his _____.

3. The big, bad bear broke the _____.

4. Harry handed the _____ to Hillary.

B. Read the following poem. Look for alliteration.

I'm an oak tree, oh so old.
Here's a story I've often told.
When the sun is high and hot,
I spread soft shade to cool the lot.
The children rest beneath the shade
And pick pretty pansies after they've played.

5. Who is the speaker in this poem? _____

6. Write the words that show alliteration. _____

_____

_____

CA **R 2.0** Reading Comprehension

The **prefixes** *re-*, *un-*, *mis-*, and *pre-* are word parts that can be added to the beginning of a base word. When a prefix is added to a base word, it changes the meaning of the base word. The prefix *re-* means "again," *pre-* means "before," *un-* mean "not or opposite," and mis- means "wrong."

re + appear = reappear   *mis + read = misread*
un + usual = unusual   *pre + pay = prepay*

Add the prefix *re-*, *pre-*, *un-*, or *mis-* to the words in the box. Then complete the sentences below with the new words.

_____ heat   _____ sure   _____ build

_____ pay   _____ spell   _____ happy

1. On my dad's birthday, my family and I decided to _____ him for all the great things he does for us.

2. We were _____ about the best way to honor him.

3. One sister wanted to _____ his workshop, which burned down in a fire.

4. I always _____ the word "restaurant."

5. My brother said, "No one is _____ when there's cake, so why don't we bake him one?"

6. "Great idea!" we all shouted. "Let's _____ the oven and start mixing the batter!"

© Macmillan/McGraw-Hill

R 1.8 Use knowledge of prefixes (e.g., *un-*, *re-*, *pre-*, *bi-*, *mis-*, *dis-*) and suffixes (e.g., *-er*, *-est*, *-ful*) to determine the meaning of words.

Ramona and Her Father
Grade 3/Unit 4   **235**

Name _____

Using the Word Study Steps

1. LOOK at the word.
2. SAY the word aloud.
3. STUDY the letters in the word.
4. WRITE the word.
5. CHECK the word.
   Did you spell the word right?
   If not, go back to step 1.

Crossword Puzzle

Write the spelling word that best matches each clue. Put the spelling word in the box that starts with the same number.

ACROSS

3. I could hear the _____ of elephant feet.
4. Harry started a bake _____ to raise money.
5. The baboon's face turned as red as a _____.
8. Keep _____ zoo ticket in case you need it later.
11. We _____ from one end of the zoo's lake to the other.
12. I sewed a small _____ of the quilt they gave to the hospital.

DOWN

1. We wrote a newsletter to stop wars and talk about _____.
2. The gorilla put _____ hand against the glass wall.
6. They are walking over _____ by the aquarium.
7. We wanted to fix the holes in the _____.
9. Every time I _____ my bike, I wore my helmet.
10. The captain raised the _____ and then we left the dock.

LC 1.8 Spell correctly one-syllable words that have blends, contractions, compounds, orthographic patterns (e.g., *qu*, consonant doubling, changing the ending of a word from -*y* to -*ies* when forming the plural), and common homophones (e.g., *hair-hare*).

© Macmillan/McGraw-Hill

Name _____

A. Proofreading

There are seven spelling mistakes in this paragraph. Circle the misspelled words. Write the words correctly on the lines below.

Volunteer Fair

Yo're invited to our annual volunteer fair. We will have lots of ideas about how to help your community. You could adopt a raod. You could raise money for an animal shelter by holding a bake sael. You could even help build a pease of the new community center. Thire are so many ideas, you won't know where to start. Its going to be quite a fair. So please join us this Friday. Yore community needs you.

1. _____   5. _____

2. _____   6. _____

3. _____   7. _____

4. _____

B. Writing Activity

Write ideas you have for helping your community. Use at least three spelling words in your paragraph.

_____

_____

_____

_____

_____

_____

© Macmillan/McGraw-Hill

LC 1.8 Spell correctly one-syllable words that have blends, contractions, compounds, orthographic patterns (e.g., *qu*, consonant doubling, changing the ending of a word from -*y* to -*ies* when forming the plural), and common homophones (e.g., *hair-hare*).

Ramona and Her Father   237
Grade 3/Unit 4

- *Is*, *are*, *am*, *was*, *were*, and *will* can be **helping verbs**.
- Use *is*, *are*, and *am* to tell about what is happening now.
  I **am** reading about plant life.
  Jeff **is** reading about plant life.
  We **are** reading about plant life.
- Use *was* and *were* to tell about what happened in the past.
  I **was** learning about sea creatures last week.
  We **were** learning about sea creatures last week.
- Use *will* to tell about something that will happen in the future.
  We **will** visit the bay tomorrow.

Write a helping verb to finish each sentence.

1. Last week we _____ learning about spartina.

2. I _____ listening to Mr. Perkins.

3. He _____ talking about the problems in the bay.

4. Kim and I _____ doing a project about native bay life.

5. I _____ looking for good photos to use.

6. We _____ finding lots of interesting information.

7. We _____ trying to find a way to use it all.

8. Kim _____ bringing her camera to the bay.

9. She _____ going to take her own pictures.

10. As we walked, I _____ feeling very surprised.

11. I _____ looking for spartina.

12. I _____ walking in some muddy water.

© Macmillan/McGraw-Hill

CA LC 1.3 Identify and use past, present, and future verb tenses properly in writing and speaking.

Name _____

- **Helping verbs** help other verbs show an action.
- Forms of *have—have*, *has*, and *had*—are used with verbs ending in *-ed*.
- Forms of *be—is*, *are*, *was*, and *were*—are used with verbs ending in *-ing*.
- *Will* helps to tell what will happen in the future.

A. Proofread the passage. Circle any incorrect helping verbs.

We has gotten on the buses very early, at 7:00 A.M. We slept on the way to Padilla Bay. We finally arrived at 9:00 A.M.

"I has never been so tired! yawned Steph.

"Wake up! said Tory. I is planning to take a class picture."

"She have taken pictures at every class trip sighed Steph.

"Hurry up!" said Ms. Harper. We has a lot of activities planned for today.

B. Writing Activity

Rewrite the passage. Write the helping verbs correctly. Add commas and quotation marks where necessary.

_____

_____

_____

_____

_____

_____

_____

© Macmillan/McGraw-Hill

LC 1.3 Identify and use past, present, and future verb tenses properly in writing and speaking.

1. Please write the following dialogue, and add quotation marks around the words that come out of each person's mouth:

Where are you going? Millie asked.

I can't tell you. It's a secret, Jameel said.

Come on! Tell me, please! begged Millie.

_____

_____

_____

2. Now do the same with the next two dialogues:

a. Does anyone want the rest of this cookie? asked Jonas.

No way, said Ramon. Those were nasty.

b. This is my favorite song. Turn it up! Stevie begged.

What? I can't hear you, yelled Marta.

_____

_____

_____

Extra Practice: Place quotation marks in the following dialogue:

Mom, have you seen my jeans? asked Danny.

No, Mom answered. Did you look in your drawer?

Oh yeah, Danny agreed. Good idea.

© Macmillan/McGraw-Hill

Name _____

> The letters **c** and **g** usually stand for a soft sound when they are followed by the vowel letters **e**, **i**, or **y**. Read the following words. Notice the **soft c** or **soft g** sound in each.
>
> gentle   engine   cell   city

A. Fill in the blank in each word with a c or a g.

> cycle   giant   iceberg   core   danger   fence   stage

1. The life _____ycle of a butterfly begins with an egg.

2. It is common to see an i_____eberg floating in the arctic waters.

3. The hot, dry climate of the desert can be a dan_____er to a hiker who is not prepared.

4. Many _____iant trees grow in the rain forest.

5. Some people build a fen_____e to protect the flowers and trees in their yard.

B. Circle the words in each group that have a soft c or soft g sound.

6. central, nice, cute, cherry

7. gem, get, germ, garden

8. ghost, guess, stage, gesture

9. circle, can't, celery, cactus

10. guppy, giraffe, gerbil, goldfish

© Macmillan/McGraw-Hill

R 1.1 Know and use complex word families when reading (e.g., *-ight*) to decode unfamiliar words.
R 1.2 Decode regular multisyllabic words.

Out of This World! • **Grade 3/Unit 4**   **241**

Name _____

A. Read the story. Then fill in each blank with the correct word from the box.

communicate   responsible   specialist   research   essential   decisions

My class is divided into teams. Although each team is working on a

different project, we all are working the same way. First, we decide who

will be _____ for getting the project done on time.

Since none of us is a _____ in our subject, we all

need to learn more. So we start by doing _____.

We _____ by speaking to one another or by e-mail

to share what we find out. We figure out if there is additional

information that is _____ for us to know. Then we

make _____ about the next step to take. Working with a

team is an interesting way to share ideas and learn about new subjects.

B. Using the clues in the story, write the definitions of these vocabulary words. Check your definitions with a dictionary.

1. specialist _____

2. decisions _____

3. essential _____

4. communicate _____

_____

 R 1.0 Word Analysis, Fluency, and Systematic Vocabulary Development

Name _____

In a story, events take place in a certain time order. The time order is called **sequence**.

Read the events. For each event, write what you think might happen next. Use clue words, such as *first*, *next*, *then*, and *finally*.

1. The kids in my class formed teams to bake a cake for the school bake sale.

   _____

2. Each team selected a type of cake to bake.

   _____

3. One team member measured and poured the ingredients into the bowl.

   _____

4. A team member poured the batter into a cake pan.

   _____

5. When the cake came out of the oven, it looked great.

   _____

   _____

© Macmillan/McGraw-Hill

As you read *Out of This World! The Ellen Ochoa Story*, fill in the Sequence Chart.

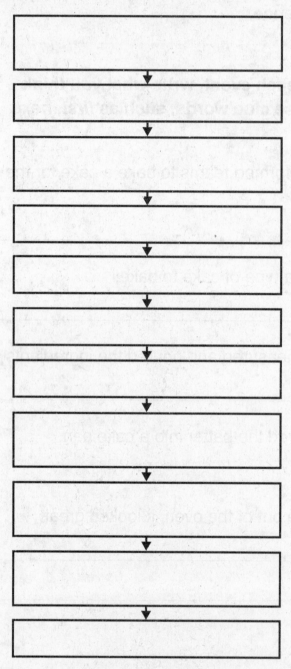

How does the information you wrote on the Sequence Chart help you better understand *Out of This World!, The Ellen Ochoa Story*?

As I read, I will pay attention to my pronunciation and phrasing.

Around the time the Pilgrims were landing in the New
10 | World, the Russians were building the first roller coaster.
19 | They built huge wooden slides. Then they poured water
28 | on them. In the cold winter, the water turned to ice. Large
40 | sleds would race down these icy slides.
47 | More than 100 years later, Empress Catherine the
54 | Great of Russia asked workmen to build her a special slide.
65 | She wanted one that could be used in the summer. In 1784,
76 | they built one that could be ridden on by a cart on wheels.
89 | Many people think this was the first real roller coaster.
99 | An artist painted Empress Catherine's slide. People
106 | said that the artist's work was fit for a queen.
116 | The first American roller coaster was built in the
125 | mountains of Pennsylvania. It was called the Mauch Chunk
134 | Switchback Railway. 136

Comprehension Check

1. Compare and contrast the first roller coaster in Russia with the roller coaster built for Empress Catherine the Great. **Compare and Contrast**

2. List one fact and one opinion about Empress Catherine's slide. **Fact and Opinion**

	Words Read	−	Number of Errors	=	Words Correct Score
First Read		−		=	
Second Read		−		=	

CA **R 1.3** Read aloud narrative and expository text fluently and accurately and with appropriate pacing, **intonation**, and expression.

Imagery is the use of words to create a detailed picture in the reader's mind.

A. **Write words you might use to describe the sky. Include words that describe how things look, feel, sound, or smell. Then write a brief poem about the sky. Make sure your poem creates a detailed picture in the reader's mind.**

Words

_____

_____

_____

Poem

_____

_____

_____

B. **Read the lines below from "Sky Bear," and then write a description of the image those lines create in your mind.**

That bear was Sky Bear,
running on through the stars.

_____

_____

_____

© Macmillan/McGraw-Hill

Name _____

> **Related words** are words that are have similar roots and
> similar meanings. A thesaurus is a dictionary of related, or
> similar, words. When you want to find the meaning of a word
> you don't know, finding a related word in a thesaurus can help
> you figure out its meaning.

**Read each sentence. Use a thesaurus to find related words to help
you figure out the meaning of the underlined words. Then write the
meaning of each underlined word.**

1. When I travel, I pack the <u>minimum</u> amount of clothing.

   Minimum means _____.

2. I have a <u>minimal</u> amount of money saved for my next vacation.

   Minimal means _____.

3. I played a <u>minor</u> part in the class play.

   Minor means _____.

4. Six <u>minus</u> three is three.

   Minus means _____.

5. My friend collects <u>miniature</u> cars.

   Miniature means _____.

6. We try to <u>minimize</u> the amount of electricity we use.

   Minimize means _____.

© Macmillan/McGraw-Hill

R 1.4 Use knowledge of antonyms, synonyms, homophones,
and homographs to determine the meanings of words.

age	nice
cents	pages
city	place
gems	price
gentle	sell
giants	space
message	

Find and Circle

Where are the spelling words?

```
P  P  X  R  A  U  G  E  M  S
R  A  W  C  I  T  Y  P  L  Y
I  G  Z  K  J  D  M  L  D  M
C  E  N  T  S  G  S  A  N  E
E  S  I  V  P  E  C  C  A  S
X  M  C  Z  A  N  D  E  G  S
K  E  E  X  C  T  O  C  E  A
Q  F  T  G  E  L  B  E  N  G
C  H  A  N  G  E  S  L  O  E
G  I  A  N  T  S  W  L  R  P
```

CA **LC 1.3** Identify and use past, present, and future verb tenses properly in writing and speaking.

© Macmillan/McGraw-Hill

A. Proofreading

There are six spelling mistakes in this paragraph. Circle the misspelled words. Write the words correctly on the lines below.

What You Can Do to Help Save the Planet

There are several ways to help take care of the nature in your town. Write to your sitti mayor about a pollution problem. This will tell him or her that you are worried about the environment. You can raise money, too. Save your extra sence. Even spare change can help buy a tree. You can then plant it on your street or in a public park. Remember to always be jentl with animals. We all have to share the same natural space. You should be nys to any wildlife you find. Never litter. This only makes the roads and grassy areas dirty. Save your plastic bottles. Buy a ginte can to put them in. When you have enough, take them in for recycling. The most important thing you can do is this: Tell others about keeping our world clean. Pass on this important mesaje to everyone you know.

1. _____   3. _____   5. _____

2. _____   4. _____   6. _____

B. Writing Activity

Write a paragraph about what you can do to help the planet. Use at least three spelling words in your paragraph.

_____

_____

_____

_____

_____

CA **LC 1.3** Identify and use past, present, and future verb tenses properly in writing and speaking.

Out of This World! • Grade 3/Unit 4   **249**

Name _____

- The past tense of regular verbs end with -ed. **Irregular verbs** have special forms to show the past tense: *I **saw** a parrot.*
- Some **irregular verbs** have another form when they follow the helping verb *have*: *I **have seen** a parrot before.*

A. Rewrite these sentences. Write the underlined verbs correctly.

1. We goed to the zoo often during the summer.

_____

2. We seened a special bird exhibit.

_____

3. The colorful birds singed loudly.

_____

4. Now they have goed to another zoo.

_____

5. Our zoo has growed in the last few years.

_____

B. Complete each sentence with the correct form of the verb.

6. We _____ to the zoo last week.   come   came

7. We _____ the polar bears being fed.   saw   seen

8. The zoo attendant _____ a bucket   bringed brought
   of food.

9. She carefully _____ the food to   gave   has gived
   the bears.

10. The bears _____ with their big paws.   ate   have eat

CA **LC 1.3** Identify and use past, present, and future verb tenses properly in writing and speaking.

Name _____

- An **irregular verb** has a special form to show the past tense.
- Some **irregular verbs** have another special form when used with the helping verb *have*.

A. Proofread the paragraphs. Circle any incorrect irregular verbs.

In class, we read about Angel Arellano. She seen that the Chaffee Zoo was having money problems. She worried about the animals at the zoo. She wrote a letter to her local newspaper. It bringed attention to the zoo. Angel have a suggestion. She has gave a dollar to the zoo. She hoped everyone else would give a dollar, too. People begun to donate money. It helped the zoo survive.

We wondered what we could change. If we all given a dollar, who could we help?

B. Writing Activity

Rewrite the paragraphs. Write the irregular verbs correctly. Make sure other verbs are also written in the correct tense.

_____

_____

_____

_____

_____

_____

_____

_____

CA **LC 1.3** Identify and use past, present, and future tense verbs properly in writing and speaking.

1. Please read the following dialogue. Notice that before the closed quotation marks, there always has to be some punctuation first. If it is a regular sentence, not a question or an exclamation, a comma goes inside the quotation marks, and a period goes at the end. **Example:**

> "I'm thirsty," said Joe.
>
> "Me too," agreed Byron.
>
> "Well, let's stop at the next store," Jo said.

2. Now copy these dialogues, adding the quotation marks, commas, and periods:

> **a.** There aren't enough seats complained Jaya
>
> Go ask those people for their extra chair Mom said
>
> I'm too shy Jaya whined
>
> **b.** This movie is boring whispered Wilson
>
> Yeah Frankie agreed
>
> Then lets get out of here Wilson said

_____

_____

_____

_____

Extra Practice: Copy this dialogue, and add the punctuation:

> I'm glad we got here before it closed Eva said
>
> We're lucky. We were almost out of gas noticed Tony
>
> I'll pump the gas, you pay ordered Eva

CA W 1.0 Writing Strategies

A **compound word** is a large word made up of two smaller words. You can often use the meaning of the smaller words to help figure out the meaning of the compound word.

A. Read each definition. Then complete the chart.

Definition	Compound Word	Two Words
1. case to store books	_____	_____ _____
2. material that covers a table	_____	_____ _____
3. the part of a day after the morning	_____	_____ _____
4. person who raises bees and collects honey	_____	_____ _____
5. no shoes or socks on your feet	_____	_____ _____
6. a book used for cooking	_____	_____ _____

B. Write sentences for two of the compound words above.

7. _____

_____

8. _____

_____

A. Choose a word from the box to correctly complete each sentence below. Write the word on the line.

down	echoes	fierce	huddle	junior	shuffles

1. Peter Penguin's father _____ instead of walks to keep Peter's egg from breaking.

2. When Peter Penguin is born, he is covered in a soft _____ coat.

3. He stays with his father to keep warm while the _____ winds blow.

4. It _____ and whistles as it blows.

5. While penguin mothers look for food, the fathers gather together in a

   _____ to stay warm.

6. When the _____ penguins are old enough, they play while the adults look for food.

B. Choose any four vocabulary words, and write a sentence for each of them on the lines below.

7. _____

8. _____

9. _____

10. _____

CA R 1.0 Word Analysis, Fluency, and Systematic Vocabulary Development

Name _____

> The **main idea** is the most important point that an author wants readers to understand. **Details** are examples and reasons that explain the main idea.

For each main idea below, write some possible supporting details.

Main Idea: It was very cold when we traveled to the Arctic.

Details:

1. The wind was fierce.

2. _____

   _____

3. _____

   _____

Main Idea: I think traveling to _____ would be exciting.

Details:

4. _____

   _____

5. _____

   _____

6. _____

   _____

CA **R 2.5** Distinguish the main idea and supporting details in expository text.

Name _____

As you read *Penguin Chick*, fill in the Main Idea and Details Chart.

Main Idea _____

_____

Detail 1: _____

Detail 2: _____

_____

Summary _____

_____

_____

_____

_____

How does the information you wrote in your Main Idea and Details Chart help you summarize *Penguin Chick*?

© Macmillan/McGraw-Hill

CA R 2.5 Distinguish the main idea and supporting details in expository text.

As I read, I will pay attention to pacing.

	A seal pup weighs about 55 pounds (25 kilograms)
7	at birth. In just ten days, the pup doubles its weight. At
19	seven weeks, it doubles its weight again. How does this
29	happen? Like all mammals, the pup drinks milk from
38	its mother's body. But seal milk is special. More than
48	half of it is fat. This helps the baby grow quickly.
59	After two weeks, the mother gives her pup a
68	swimming lesson in the cold Arctic waters. The pup
77	shuffles to the water's edge. The mother pushes her
86	young one into the water. Soon the pup is swimming. 96

Comprehension Check

1. How much would a seal pup weigh after ten days? **Draw Conclusions**

2. How does a seal pup learn to swim? **Main Idea and Details**

	Words Read	–	Number of Errors	=	Words Correct Score
First Read		–		=	
Second Read		–		=	

© Macmillan/McGraw-Hill

R 1.3 Read aloud narrative and expository text fluently and accurately and with appropriate **pacing**, intonation, and expression.

> **Imagery** is the use of words to create a picture in the reader's mind.

A. Read the poem. Then complete the chart.

Penguins

The penguin is a funny clown
Dressed up in black and white.

He slips and slides on glassy ice
And chatters with delight

Then zips and darts through deep blue sea
To catch a tasty bite.

Imagery Describing the Penguin's Appearance	Imagery Describing the Penguin's Movement	Imagery Describing Nature

B. Think of an animal you know. Write a description of it. Be sure to use imagery to help readers picture the animal you're describing.

_____

_____

_____

CA R 2.0 Reading Comprehension

Homographs are words that have different meanings but the same spelling. The meaning of a homograph depends on how it is used.

For example, the word *down* can mean two different things.

The leaves on the tree began to fall **down**.

When baby birds hatch, they are covered with soft **down**.

Use the homographs in the box to answer the following questions.

tear	palm	clip	fan

1. What is a part of your hand? _____

2. What is a drop of water that comes from your eye? _____

3. What do you do to make hair shorter? _____

4. What do you wave to cool yourself off? _____

5. What is a tree in hot tropical areas? _____

6. What is a rip in your jacket? _____

7. What holds papers together? _____

8. What do you call a person who loves sports? _____

R 1.4 Use knowledge of antonyms, synonyms, homophones, and **homographs** to determine the meanings of words.

Penguin Chick • **Grade 3/Unit 5**   **259**

Name _____

Using the Word Study Steps

1. LOOK at the word.

2. SAY the word aloud.

3. STUDY the letters in the word.

4. WRITE the word.

5. CHECK the word.
   Did you spell the word right?
   If not, go back to step 1.

A. Compound Riddles

Join two words from the riddle to make a compound word.

1. A foot that is bare _____

2. The light of the day _____

3. Paper where you read the news _____

4. The day of your birth _____

5. The house of a bird _____

6. The way someone will do your hair _____

7. Time during the day _____

8. A ball you shoot in a basket _____

9. A book in which you write a note _____

10. Place for walks on the side of the road _____

B. Make a Compound Word

A compound word is made up of two or more smaller words.
Draw lines connecting the words that form other compound words.

11. some   coach

12. air   one

13. head   time

14. some   plane

15. stage   light

LC 1.8 Spell correctly one-syllable words that have blends, contractions, compounds, orthographic patterns (e.g., *qu*, consonant doubling, changing the ending of a word from -*y* to -*ies* when forming the plural), and common homophones (e.g., *hair-hare*).

© Macmillan/McGraw-Hill

Name _____

A. Proofreading

There are six spelling mistakes in the letter. Circle the misspelled words. Write the words correctly on the lines below.

Dear Mr. Taylor,

I am writing to you for some advice on a business idea I had. I read about your sports store in the nuespapper. You seem like sumone who could help me.

I had the idea one day while I was walking home. My feet were hurting because I had been playing basckettebal bearfoot. My idea was to create a mailing list of customers. With each name, you could also list the person's burthdea. Your store could use the list to send letters reminding your customers to buy a new pair of shoes. You could even include a coupon! Maybe you could sell the list to different stores in town. The barber shop could send a coupon for a haredoe.

What do you think? If you are interested, please write to me.

Regards,
Josh Curtain

1. _____   4. _____

2. _____   5. _____

3. _____   6. _____

B. Writing Activity

Write a paragraph describing a business you would like to start. Use at least four spelling words in your description.

_____

_____

_____

_____

LC 1.8 Spell correctly one-syllable words that have blends, contractions, compounds, orthographic patterns (e.g., *qu*, consonant doubling, changing the ending of a word from *-y* to *-ies* when forming the plural), and common homophones (e.g., *hair-hare*).

Penguin Chick • **Grade 3/Unit 5** **261**

Name _____

> • Plural **pronouns** are *we, you, they, us,* and *them.*

Read each sentence. Replace the underlined word or words with a plural pronoun. Use clues in the sentences to help you decide.

1. James, Sarah, and I decided to start a cookie business.

   _____

2. Have you and your friends ever tried to start a business?

   _____

3. James and Sarah made the cookies. _____

4. I painted signs while I waited for James and Sarah. _____

5. Then there was a phone call for James, Sarah, and me.

   _____

6. James, Sarah, and I had our first customers! _____

7. The cookies were still warm from the oven. _____

8. Sarah carefully wrapped the cookies. _____

9. James, Sarah, and I delivered the cookies to our customers.

   _____

10. The people were delighted and promised to order more.

   _____

© Macmillan/McGraw-Hill

CA **LC 1.0** Written and Oral English Language Conventions

- A **pronoun** is a word that takes the place of one or more nouns.
- A pronoun must match the noun that it replaces.
- Singular pronouns are *I, you, he, she, it, me, him,* and *her.*
- Plural pronouns are *we, you, they, us,* and *them.*

A. Proofread the paragraph. Circle any incorrect pronouns.

We recently read *Boom Town*. They is the story of a girl named amanda, who lived in california in the 1800s. Her helped her town grow by starting a pie business. Us decided to try the gooseberry pie recipe in the book. Mom suggested using blueberries instead. Then Mom thought there wasn't enough sugar. Him kept adding more. I thought there weren't enough berries. You piled them so high that there wasn't enough dough to cover them. Then me forgot to turn on the oven. No wonder the pie took so long to bake!

B. Rewrite the paragraph with the correct pronouns. Make sure all proper nouns and *I* are capitalized.

_____

_____

_____

_____

_____

_____

_____

_____

© Macmillan/McGraw-Hill

CA **LC 1.0** Written and Oral English Language Conventions

Name _____

1. Read:

Jake ran to catch the ball.

The batter hit the ball into the outfield.

It bounced out of his glove.

He scooped the ball up and threw it to Kevin.

2. Think: Are these sentences in an order that makes sense?

3. Write the sentences in order:

1. _____

2. _____

3. _____

4. _____

The **inflectional endings** -*es* or -*ed* can be added to the end of a verb to show when an action happens.

If the letter before the *y* is a consonant, change the *y* to *i*, and add -*es* or -*ed*. Notice how the word *worry* changes to *worries* and *worried*.

hurry	supply	study	dry	display	copy

Fill in the blank in each sentence with the correct inflectional form of a verb from the box. Think about when you need to change the *y* to *i*, and add -*es* or -*ed*.

1. Club members _____ to catch the bus for their trip downtown.

2. Ana _____ hard for the quiz on transportation.

3. Walt _____ old photographs and uses them as guides when he draws antique cars.

4. Marla's grandmother _____ her teacup collection on a shelf in the living room.

5. I have to wait until my shirt _____ before I can go outside and play again.

6. The conductor _____ all the passengers with blankets when the heat went off.

CA R 1.2 Decode regular multisyllabic words.

Fill in the blank with the correct word from the box.
Some words will be used more than once.

architects	shallow	structures
contain	retreats	shelter

1. Animals are like _____ because they build their own homes.

2. Termites build tall _____.

3. Some _____ study animal homes for ideas about solving problems with buildings.

4. The tortoise builds a _____ hole to keep cool.

5. A polar bear, however, needs a very different type of

   _____.

6. If you come across a spider's web, be careful because it may

   _____ an insect.

7. A turtle _____ into its shell when it senses danger.

8. A hermit crab finds _____ in an empty shell.

CA R 1.0 Word Analysis, Fluency, and Systematic Vocabulary Development

Nonfiction articles that have information about a topic often use **description**. In this description, the author uses **relevant facts and details** to identify characteristics or qualities that help you understand the topic. These examples and details also help you remember what you read.

Read the passage below. Summarize it by writing the main topic, the example, and any supporting details on the lines.

    Trees are important habitats for gray squirrels. The young are raised in holes in the trees while the older squirrels usually nest in piles of leaves near the trees. The trees provide many sources of food for the gray squirrels, such as acorns, hickory nuts, insects, flower buds, bark, and roots. Trees are very important to the gray squirrel.

Topic: _____

_____

Example: _____

Detail: _____

Detail: _____

Detail: _____

Name _____

As you read *Animal Homes*, fill in the Description Web.

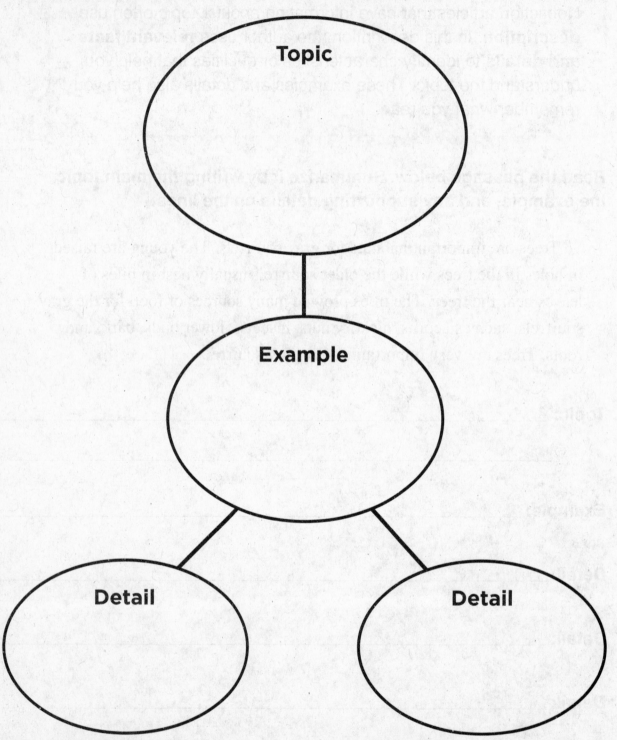

Topic

Example

Detail

Detail

How does the information you wrote in this Description Web help you summarize *Animal Homes*?

CA R 2.0 Reading Comprehension

Name _____

As I read, I will pay attention to pacing and phrasing.

	Many different kinds of animals build their own
8	homes. Their homes are structures that shelter them
16	from the cold and the rain. They are also places where
27	they can retreat from danger. Beavers build lodges, bees
36	build hives, and birds build incredible nests where they
45	hatch their eggs and raise their babies.
52	Have you ever seen a bird's nest? Some are made of
63	twigs and are round and shallow. Others are made of
73	grass and are long and deep. Still others are made from
84	mud and look like small cups. There are even birds that
95	use their own saliva, or spit, when they build a nest.
106	Many birds' nests contain feathers and hair. This makes the
116	nest a soft place for their babies, or chicks, to sleep. Birds
128	are some of the most amazing **architects** in the animal
138	world! 139

Comprehension Check

1. Compare and contrast different birds' nests. **Compare and Contrast**

2. What does the word *saliva* mean? **Context Clues**

	Words Read	–	Number of Errors	=	Words Correct Score
First Read		–		=	
Second Read		–		=	

© Macmillan/McGraw-Hill

CA **R 1.3** Read aloud narrative and expository text fluently and accurately and with appropriate **pacing**, intonation, and expression.

Directions help you do something by following steps in a process. The steps are usually numbered so that you can easily follow each step from first to last.

A. The directions for making a dragon puppet are written below, but they are out of order. Next to each step, write a number from 1 to 6 to show the correct order.

Materials: colored paper, scissors, crayons or markers, glue, and two straws

____ Cut out the head and tail, and glue one to each end of the body.

____ Finally, glue the straws onto the backs of the tail and body.

____ First, fold a piece of paper in half the long way. Cut along the folded line.

____ Draw a head and a tail on another sheet of paper.

____ Then fold each piece of paper like an accordion.

____ Glue the two folded pieces together to make a long body.

B. Now that you have figured out how to make a dragon puppet, write down the steps you would take to make an animal costume for a costume party.

1. _____

2. _____

3. _____

4. _____

5. _____

CA **R 2.1** Use titles, tables of contents, chapter headings, glossaries, and indexes to locate information in text.

Name _____

Homophones are words that sound the same but have
different meanings and different spellings

A. Circle the correct word to complete each sentence.

1. Animals build many different kinds of homes to meet (their, there) needs.

2. The need for shelter is one of the (main, mane) reasons animals
   build homes.

3. Shelter is (knot, not) the only reason animals build homes.

4. Animals build homes to have a safe place and to keep warm, (too, to).

5. It takes a (whole, hole) lot of time to build a beaver's home.

6. Animals use materials they find in the area (too, to) build their homes.

7. A bird may use hair from a horse's (main, mane) to build its nest.

8. A (whole, hole) in the ground can be a home for some animals.

9. Some birds make a (knot, not) out of grass and use it to build their home.

10. Animals whose homes are underground usually spend the winter
    (their, there).

B. Write the correct homophone next to each word below.

11. cells _____   14. be _____

12. way _____   15. two _____

13. son _____   16. deer _____

R 1.4 Use knowledge of antonyms, synonyms, homophones, and
homographs to determine the meaning of words.

dried	playing
dries	studied
drying	studies
hurried	studying
hurries	tried
hurrying	trying
played	

Find and Circle

Where are the spelling words?

```
T  R  Y  I  N  G  E  H  B  V  X  M
X  E  R  Q  P  Y  T  U  J  H  H  H
S  T  U  D  I  E  D  R  Z  N  U  J
T  R  I  E  S  R  R  R  U  E  R  F
P  I  V  Q  U  Y  I  I  Y  D  R  S
U  E  D  W  N  H  E  E  G  R  Y  S
J  D  S  E  B  M  S  D  D  Y  I  T
P  L  A  Y  E  D  J  K  R  I  N  U
L  O  P  W  P  L  A  Y  I  N  G  D
A  H  U  R  R  I  E  S  E  G  P  I
Y  X  V  D  J  F  M  W  D  A  Q  E
S  T  U  D  Y  I  N  G  S  C  Y  S
```

CA **LC 1.8** Spell correctly one-syllable words that have blends, contractions, compounds, orthographic patterns (e.g., *qu*, consonant doubling, changing the ending of a word from *-y* to *-ies* when forming the plural), and common homophones (e.g., *hair-hare*).

Name _____

A. There are six spelling mistakes in this paragraph. Circle the misspelled words. Write the words correctly on the lines below.

Our class is studieing dances performed by people around the world. People dance for many reasons: to celebrate good things, to welcome visitors, or just to have fun.

We watched videos of children who were plaing and dancing with their friends. They tryed to jump as high and spin as fast as they could. It looked like fun!

I like to dance, too. I take ballet lessons. I am almost always late for class. Sometimes my tights have not dryed out from being washed. Other times I am hurrieing to finish my homework. My sister studys tap dancing. When I get older, I will learn other kinds of dancing too.

I know why people all over the world dance. It's fun and it's good exercise!

1. _____   4. _____

2. _____   5. _____

3. _____   6. _____

B. Writing Activity

Imagine that you are the coach of a soccer team. Write the speech that you would give your players before the big game. Use at least four spelling words in your description.

_____

_____

_____

_____

_____

LC 1.8 Spell correctly one-syllable words that have blends, contractions, compounds, orthographic patterns (e.g., *qu*, consonant doubling, changing the ending of a word from -*y* to -*ies* when forming the plural), and common homophones (e.g., *hair-hare*).

© Macmillan/McGraw-Hill

Name _____

> • Use an **object pronoun** after an action verb or after a word such as *for*, *at*, *of*, *with*, or *to*.
> • *Me, you, him, her, it, us,* and *them* are object pronouns.

Read the sentences. Choose the correct pronoun in parentheses to complete each sentence. Write the pronoun.

1. Ms. Robinson read _____ *Beatrice's Goat.*   (us, we)

2. It is about a girl named Beatrice and the goat given   (her, she)

   to _____.

3. The story showed how Beatrice's family took the   (it, its)

   goat's milk and sold _____ to raise money.

4. Beatrice's family used the money to send   (her, she)

   _____ to school.

5. Josh listened to the story with _____.   (I, me)

6. I told _____ I had met some goats last   (he, him)
   summer at a farm.

7. We played with _____ a lot while we   (they, them)
   were there.

8. "I will show _____ a picture of a baby   (you, your)
   goat," I said.

© Macmillan/McGraw-Hill

CA **LC 1.2** Identify subjects and verbs that are in agreement and identify and use **pronouns**, adjectives, compound words, and articles correctly in writing and speaking.

Name _____

- Use a **subject pronoun** as the subject of a sentence.
- *I, you, he, she, it, we,* and *they* are subject pronouns.
- Use an **object pronoun** after an action verb or after a word such as *for, at, of, with,* or *to.*
- *Me, you, him, her, it, us,* and *them* are object pronouns.

A. Proofread the paragraphs below. Circle any pronouns that are used incorrectly.

    My class read a book called *Beatrice's Goat.* Us learned how the gift of a goat from Heifer International helped Beatrice go to school. The book had an influence on we all. Everyone wanted to do something to help others.

    We decided to make and sell farm-animal pins. Everyone in town loved they. Them helped the class raise a lot of money. We were glad to give the money to Heifer International. We felt good—we were helping they. Maybe yous can help someone, too!

B. Rewrite the paragraph. Write the pronouns correctly.

_____

_____

_____

_____

_____

_____

_____

LC 1.2 Identify subjects and verbs that are in agreement and identify and use **pronouns**, adjectives, compound words, and articles correctly in writing and speaking.

Animal Homes
Grade 3/Unit 5
275

Name _____

1. Review:

There are many ways to start a journal entry:

Four Types of Leads
Action
Dialogue
Observation
Question

2. Read:

"Why are you eating my sandwich?" Jim demanded.

"I didn't know it was yours," Cara replied. _____
Type of Lead

Have you ever been lost in a book? _____
Type of Lead

The motorcycle rider slammed on the brakes. _____
Type of Lead

I noticed the rain as it pattered softly on the window. _____
Type of Lead

3. Write the correct type of lead next to each sentence above.

Name _____

A syllable is a word part with one vowel sound. A **closed syllable** ends with a consonant. In most closed syllables, the vowel has a short vowel sound.

A. Circle the words that have two closed syllables.

1. sudden   agent   7. human   upset

2. suspect   focus   8. fossil   bonus

3. baby   basket   9. basic   plastic

4. cactus   lady   10. music   sunset

5. oval   tunnel   11. content   cozy

6. delay   subject   12. donate   cabin

B. Use a word from the box to complete each sentence. Choose a word with two closed syllables.

| tiger | rabbit | seahorse | dolphin |

13. A _____ is a wild animal that lives on land.

14. A _____ lives in the ocean.

A. Read the story. Then fill in each blank with the correct word from the box.

> crucial   adjust   survive   source   unpredictable

Sometimes the weather can be _____. Weather

changes can cause problems for animals in the wild. The animals have

to _____ to changes in temperature. If the weather gets

too cold, the animals need to find ways to _____.

Some animals may huddle together. Staying close to each other provides a

_____ of heat. It is _____ for the

animals to find shelter so they can be safe from the cold. Since animals are

clever, they usually find ways to adapt to any weather.

B. Using the clues in the story, write the definitions of these vocabulary words. Check your definitions with a dictionary.

1. crucial _____

2. adjust _____

3. survive _____

4. source _____

5. unpredictable _____

CA **R 1.0** Word Analysis, Fluency, and Systematic Vocabulary Development

Name _____

- A **cause** is an event or an action that makes something happen. An **effect** is something that happens because of an event or an action.
- To identify cause and effect, look for signal words, such as *cause*, *effect*, *because*, *due to*, *since*, *if*, and *when*.

Read this paragraph and answer the questions below.

Animals often have to move because of changes in their habitat. When trees are cut down, birds can lose their nesting places. They move to a new place where there are more trees to nest in. In dry weather, ponds sometimes dry up. Because some animals like frogs need water to survive, they move to find a place with water. When people build more homes in an area, there are fewer places where animals can find food and water. This causes the animals to move to places where they can get what they need to survive. When animals move to a new area, they can cause problems for the plants and animals that already live there.

1. What causes animals to have to move? _____

   _____

2. When trees are cut down, what effect does this have on birds? _____

   _____

3. What can cause animals like frogs to move? _____

4. What is the effect of people building more homes? _____

   _____

© Macmillan/McGraw-Hill

Name _____

As you read *Call of the Wild*, fill in the Cause and Effect Chart.

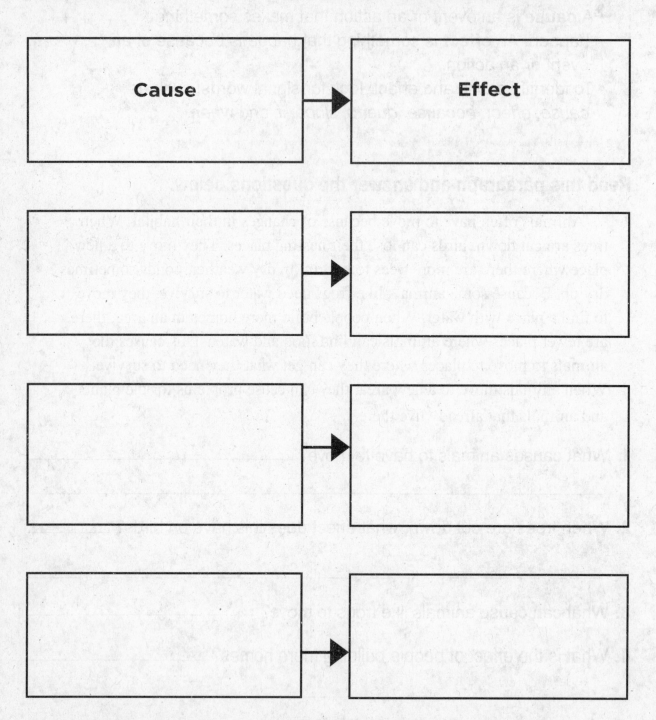

Cause → **Effect**

How does the information you wrote on the Cause and Effect Chart help you better understand *Call of the Wild*?

CA R 2.0 Reading Comprehension

As I read, I will pay attention to phrasing.

	Winds scream. Rain pelts down. Buildings shudder.
7	Trees sway back and forth. Branches break and fall to the
18	ground. It's a hurricane!
22	You've probably seen pictures or images of hurricanes
30	in a newspaper or on TV. What makes a storm a hurricane?
42	A hurricane is a storm with very strong winds and
52	heavy rain. It starts over warm waters in an ocean. The
63	storm might take the shape of a circle or an oval. It can be
77	up to 400 miles (640 km) wide.
82	How do people prepare for hurricanes? How do
90	"hurricane heroes" do their work? They do their jobs in
100	offices and shelters. They are important before, during, and
109	after a big storm. They help save lives.
117	How do people find out if a bad storm is coming?
128	Air Force pilots called hurricane hunters fly into the
137	eye of the storm. 141

Comprehension Check

1. What is a hurricane? **Main Idea and Details**

2. Who are hurricane hunters? **Main Idea and Details**

	Words Read	–	Number of Errors	=	Words Correct Score
First Read		–		=	
Second Read		–		=	

CA **R 1.3** Read aloud narrative and expository text fluently and accurately
and with appropriate pacing, intonation, and expression.

Skim means to read over a passage quickly to identify the main ideas. **Scan** means to search through a passage for key words or ideas.

Skim and scan the passage to help you answer the following questions.

The earth is warming quickly. This causes problems for all living things. Sea ice in the Arctic is melting about three weeks earlier than it did 30 years ago. This is not good for the people who live there. Their homes are damaged by the melting ice. They also have fewer animals to hunt for food. Polar bears, seals, and other arctic animals are having problems, too. The ice cap is getting smaller, so there is less room for them to live. Their food supply is disappearing, so they have to move to new places to find food.

1. What is the main idea of this passage? _____

_____

2. What did you do to figure out the main idea? _____

_____

3. Draw a circle around the key words. How did they help you figure out the

main idea? _____

4. How much earlier is sea ice in the Arctic melting than it did 30 years

ago? _____

© Macmillan/McGraw-Hill

CA **R 2.0** Reading Comprehension

Name _____

Cause/Effect Writing Frame

A. Summarize *Call of the Wild*. **Use the Cause/Effect Writing Frame below.**

Many animals have had to adapt to their environments to survive.

Arctic foxes have adapted to living in the Arctic **because** _____

_____.

The **result** of this is _____

_____.

The breaks of the Galapagos Island finches have changed **because** _____

_____.

The **result** of this is _____

_____.

Other animals that have changed are _____

_____

They have changed **because** _____

_____.

B. Rewrite the completed summary on another sheet of paper. Keep it as a model for writing a summary of an article or selection using this text structure.

Synonyms are words with the same or similar meanings. Writers often help you understand the meaning of a new word by using a synonym in the same sentence or in a nearby sentence. A thesaurus can also help you find synonyms for a new word.

Read each pair of sentences. Look for a synonym of the word in dark type in the second sentence. Write it on the line below.

1. Plants **thrive** when they get enough food, water, and sunlight. With the right conditions, the plants will grow.

   Synonym:_____

2. Our tomato plants **withered** last week when there was no rain. We were sad to see how much they drooped by the end of the week.

   Synonym:_____

3. Sometimes caterpillars can be a **nuisance** in the garden. In fact, most gardeners think caterpillars are pests.

   Synonym:_____

4. Sometimes, plants have to **adapt** to new conditions. If the plants can't change, they won't survive.

   Synonym:_____

5. Our plants **flourished** when we gave them some plant food. I think they grew five inches in a week!

   Synonym:_____

6. Soon we will **harvest** our tomatoes. My sister and I have a contest to see who can pick the most.

   Synonym:_____

CA **R 1.4** Use knowledge of antonyms, synonyms, homophones, and homographs to determine the meanings of words.

Name _____

Using the Word Study Steps

1. LOOK at the word.

2. SAY the word aloud.

3. STUDY the letters in the word.

4. WRITE the word.

5. CHECK the word.
   Did you spell the word right?
   If not, go back to step 1.

A. Circle the Rhyming Word

Circle the word in each row that rhymes with the word in dark type.

1. **swallow**	fellow	follow	swell
2. **better**	letter	ladder	batter
3. **flutter**	chapter	flatter	butter
4. **yellow**	fellow	yelled	follow
5. **polite**	police	invite	polish
6. **camel**	mammal	maple	manage
7. **habit**	bedtime	rather	rabbit
8. **Monday**	birthday	today	Sunday

B. X the Word

Put an X on the word in each row that does not fit the pattern.

9. napkin	basket	rabbit	tried
10. Sunday	drying	number	butter
11. studies	follow	problem	stopping
12. chicken	sick	click	jumping

© Macmillan/McGraw-Hill

CA LC 1.8 Spell correctly one-syllable words that have blends,
contractions, compounds, orthographic patterns (e.g., *qu*, consonant
doubling, changing the ending of a word from -y to -ies when forming
the plural), and common homophones (e.g., *hair-hare*).

Name _____

A. There are six spelling mistakes in this story. Circle the misspelled words. Write the words correctly on the lines below.

The Great Rescue

One Sonday afternoon my family went on a picnic. My mother packed our lunch in a big bascett. We found a shady spot under a tree and ate fried chikin and bread with bauter.

After lunch, my sister and I took a canoe out on the lake. We were drifting along when suddenly my sister screamed. I looked over to see what the problime was. There was a hole in the bottom of the boat. The canoe was filling up with water.

Luckily, our parents saw us and ran for help. Another person, who was also on a picnic, said he would help. This fine fello swam out to the canoe with two life jackets. He held out a rope for us to grab onto, and then he dragged us to shore. He was our hero!

It was an exciting end to an almost peaceful picnic.

1. _____   4. _____

2. _____   5. _____

3. _____   6. _____

B. Writing Activity

Imagine that you are on a picnic and something unexpected happens. Who steps in to help you? Write a short story about it, using at least four spelling words.

_____

_____

_____

_____

CA **LC 1.8** Spell correctly one-syllable words that have blends, contractions, compounds, orthographic patterns (e.g., *qu*, consonant doubling, changing the ending of a word from -y to -ies when forming the plural), and common homophones (e.g., *hair-hare*).

Name _____

- The verbs *have* and *be* have special forms in the present tense.

Forms of *have*		Forms of *be*	
I have	You have	I am	You are
He has	We have	He is	We are
She has	They have	She is	They are
It has		It is	

Write the correct form of the verb in parentheses to complete each sentence.

1. I _____ on our school newspaper staff this year.   (be)

2. I _____ many different jobs to do at our newspaper.   (have)

3. It _____ fun to learn about putting a paper together.   (be)

4. We _____ help from Ms. Lawrence and Mr. Green.   (have)

5. He _____ in charge of the photography.   (be)

6. She _____ there to help us with writing.   (be)

7. They _____ many good ideas.   (have)

8. He _____ several types of cameras.   (have)

9. She _____ friends at real newspapers.   (have)

10. We _____ happy to visit their offices today.   (be)

11. It _____ a lot different than I expected.   (be)

12. Do you _____ a newspaper at your school?   (have)

© Macmillan/McGraw-Hill

LC 1.2 Identify subjects and verbs that are in agreement and identify and use pronouns, adjectives, compound words, and articles correctly in writing and speaking.

- A **present-tense** verb must agree with its **subject pronoun**.
- Add -s to most present-tense action verbs when you use the pronouns *he*, *she*, and *it*.
- Do not add -s to present-tense action verbs when you use the pronouns *I*, *we*, *you*, and *they*.
- The verbs *have* and *be* have special forms.

A. Proofread the paragraph. Circle any verbs that do not agree with their subject pronouns.

This summer, my best friend and I are doing something new. We puts out our own newspaper every week. It be only four pages long, but it take a lot of time to do it well. I are in charge of the stories. Curt take all the pictures. Each week, I has to find new stories for our paper. I talk to people in town. I look for interesting things. Curt take his's camera everywhere. He have more pictures than pages!

B. Writing Activity

Rewrite the paragraph. Make sure the verbs agree with their subject pronouns. Fix incorrect possessive pronouns, too.

_____

_____

_____

_____

_____

_____

_____

CA **LC 1.2** Identify subjects and verbs that are in agreement and identify and use pronouns, adjectives, compound words, and articles correctly in writing and speaking.

Writing Rubric

4 Excellent	3 Good	2 Fair	1 Unsatisfactory
Ideas and Content/ Genre	Ideas and Content/ Genre	Ideas and Content/ Genre	Ideas and Content/ Genre
Organization and Focus	Organization and Focus	Organization and Focus	Organization and Focus
Sentence Structure/ Fluency	Sentence Structure/ Fluency	Sentence Structure/ Fluency	Sentence Structure/ Fluency
Conventions	Conventions	Conventions	Conventions
Word Choice	Word Choice	Word Choice	Word Choice
Voice	Voice	Voice	Voice
Presentation	Presentation	Presentation	Presentation

When added to the end of a verb, the **inflectional endings -s**, **-es**, **-ed**, and **-ing** show when action happens, as in: *He calls his sister often*; *He called yesterday*; *He is calling right now*.

If a word ends in *e*, drop the *e* before adding *-ed* or *-ing*, as in *decided*, *deciding*. If a word has the CVC pattern, double the final consonant before adding *-ed* or *-ing*, as in *ripped*, *ripping*.

Add the inflectional endings *-s or -es*, *-ed*, and *-ing* to the words below. Then write a sentence using one form of the word.

1. drop _____

_____

2. wrap _____

_____

3. stomp _____

_____

4. clear _____

_____

5. name _____

_____

6. stop _____

_____

© Macmillan/McGraw-Hill

CA R 1.2 Decode regular multisyllabic words.

Fill in each blank with the word from the box that makes the most sense. Some words may be used more than once.

boasting	conversation	interrupted
seized	rebuild	scrambled

Whenever you read a _____ between two animals, you know that you are reading a fantasy. My friend wrote a story about a peacock that would not stop _____ about his beautiful tail feathers. The peacock's bragging was suddenly _____ by a noisy bluebird. The bird complained that last night's storm had blown his nest out of the tree. Now he had to find twigs and grasses to _____ the nest. The peacock _____ the opportunity to spread his feathers and sway back and forth with his head held high. He kept _____ about how grand he looked. The bluebird just flew away.

Then a squirrel _____ by and sat in front of the peacock. "Watch me. I bet you can't do this," he said, as he juggled five acorns high in the air. The peacock said, "What a show-off you are! Stop your _____!"

When you **make judgments**, it means you form an opinion about the actions of characters in a story. Readers should use story details and experience to support their judgments. Making judgments helps you understand plot development.

Read the passage, and answer the questions below.

Eli Whitney invented the cotton gin in 1793. Before the machine was invented, people had to use their hands to separate the cotton fibers from the seeds. This process took a lot of time and was very expensive. For these reasons, cotton was not yet important in America. Whitney's new technology now meant that a machine could process large amounts of cotton faster and cheaper than any human. In 1790, the United States. shipped 25,000 pounds of raw cotton fiber to England, where the fibers were turned into cloth. By 1858, the United States was shipping over one billion pounds of cotton fiber to English factories.

Back in the United States, the South was turning into a "sea of cotton." More enslaved people than ever before were needed to work in the cotton fields. In Mississippi and Louisiana, the number of enslaved workers rose from 8,000 in 1785 to 450,000 in 1858. In England, the factories needed more cheap workers. Children as young as seven worked at the weaving looms making cloth out of cotton fibers. Sometimes the children fell into the looms. The lives of English factory workers and enslaved Americans were alike in many ways.

1. What judgment did people make about cotton before the cotton gin?

   _____

   _____

2. What judgment can you make about the cotton gin? Explain whether you

   think it was a helpful or harmful invention. _____

   _____

CA **R 3.3** Determine what characters are like by what they say or do and by how the author or illustrator portrays them.

Name _____

As you read *Wilbur's Boast*, fill in the Judgment Chart.

Action		Judgment
	→	

	→	

	→	

How does the information you wrote in this Judgment Chart help you understand plot development in *Wilbur's Boast*?

© Macmillan/McGraw-Hill

R 3.3 Determine what characters are like by what they say or do and by how the author or illustrator portrays them.

As I read, I will pay attention to pacing and phrasing.

	Mike Drake worked as the night custodian at Riverside School.
10	Each night, he went from classroom to classroom, mopping and
20	cleaning. Mike liked to take his late-night snack break when he got
32	to Room 4. While he ate his snack, he taught Artie, the Room 4
44	parakeet, to talk. He gave Artie a lesson almost every night.
55	"Yoo-hoo, Artie." Mike seized the cover of the parakeet's cage
65	and pulled it off. "It is your good buddy, Mike. How is my pretty
79	bird?"
80	Mike always interrupted Artie's sleep. Artie was never prepared
89	for this nightly wake-up call. He blinked and looked around.
99	"Artie, are you ready for your vocabulary lesson?" asked Mike.
109	"Okay," said Artie. He hopped onto his swing and began to sway.
121	"Who is that pretty bird?" said Mike. "What is that pretty bird's
133	name?"
134	"R-T," said Artie. The swing squeaked as it went back and
145	forth. 146

Comprehension Check

1. Why does Mike Drake like to take his snack break in Room 4? **Plot Development**

2. What does the word *seized* mean? **Context Clues**

	Words Read	–	Number of Errors	=	Words Correct Score
First Read		–		=	
Second Read		–		=	

CA **R 1.3** Read aloud narrative and expository text fluently and accurately and with appropriate **pacing**, intonation, and expression.

Name _____

Personification is giving human characteristics to an animal or thing. Examples:

a talking tree   a smiling sun
a frog that swings on a trapeze   a cow that sings

Fables are stories that teach a lesson and often have animal characters that talk and act like people.

A **moral** is a lesson that a fable teaches. The reader can apply a moral to his or her own personal experiences.

Read the fable below. Then answer the questions.

One day an ant was drinking from the river. He fell in and was carried along by the stream. A dove saw the ant and threw a twig into the water. The ant crawled onto the twig and made it safely to the bank of the river. "Thank you," said the ant. "You saved my life." Soon after, the ant spotted a hunter who was aiming his rifle toward the dove. The ant crawled onto the hunter's foot and bit him hard. The hunter dropped his rifle. The dove's life was saved.

1. How does the author use personification in the fable? _____

_____

_____

2. What is the moral of this story? _____

_____

_____

R 3.3 Determine what characters are like by what they say or do and by how the author or illustrator portrays them.
R 3.4 Determine the underlying theme or author's message in fiction and nonfiction text.

Wilbur's Boast • Grade 3/Unit 5   **295**

Name _____

The **prefixes *re-*, *pre-*, *un-*,** and ***dis-*** are word parts that can be added to the beginning of base words to form new words with new meanings. The prefix *re-* means "to do again," *pre-* means "before," and *dis-* and *un-* mean "not or opposite."

re + appear = reappear   pre + cut = precut
un + even = uneven   dis + order = disorder

**Add the prefix *re-*, *pre-*, *un-*, or *dis-* to the words in the box.
Then complete the sentences below with the new words.**

_____ cycling   _____ heat   _____ obey

_____ cover   _____ happy   _____ trained

1. I need to _____ the oven before I start baking.

2. It would be good for my owner to train me so I do not

   _____ him.

3. My owner needs to be _____ so she can better understand what a puppy like me needs.

4. I know that my kind owner would never be _____ enough to sell me.

5. I love to go with my owner when he drives to the _____ center with used cans and bottles.

6. I hope that she will _____ my dish before she puts it on the floor.

CA R 1.8 Use knowledge of prefixes (e.g., *un-*, *re-*, *pre-*, *bi-*, *mis-*, *dis-*) and suffixes (e.g., *-er*, *-est*, *-ful*) to determine the meaning of words.

© Macmillan/McGraw-Hill

Name _____

Using the Word Study Steps

1. LOOK at the word.

2. SAY the word aloud.

3. STUDY the letters in the word.

4. WRITE the word.

5. CHECK the word.
   Did you spell the word right?
   If not, go back to step 1.

X the Word

Put an X on the word that does not fit the pattern in each row.

1. named	jumped	grabbed	stirs
2. wrapped	wraps	lined	hurried
3. lives	hopes	gives	giving
4. drop	dropping	playing	wrapping
5. dances	dancing	hoping	running
6. naming	shake	shaking	splitting
7. dropped	wrapped	hope	hoped
8. wraps	names	dances	play
9. digging	forgets	naming	losing
10. wrap	hoped	stopped	mopped

LC 1.8 Spell correctly one-syllable words that have blends,
contractions, compounds, orthographic patterns (e.g., *qu*, consonant
doubling, changing the ending of a word from -*y* to -*ies* when forming
the plural), and common homophones (e.g., *hair-hare*).

A. There are six spelling mistakes in the speech below. Circle the misspelled words. Write the words correctly on the lines below.

Welcome, students, parents, and teachers, to this assembly!

This year our school is giving an award to the student who has done the most to help others. One student has shown us that it does not matter what you are naimmed or where you live. Everyone can find ways to help others.

She hoopes to be a role model for other students. Her actions prove that even small things can make a difference. Our winner spent time droping food off at a soup kitchen with her family and wraping small gifts for people in a nursing home. She has also shared her talents with others, danceing in performances at a local hospital.

For all these reasons and more, we are nameing Susan Harper our student of the year!

1. _____   4. _____

2. _____   5. _____

3. _____   6. _____

B. Writing Activity

Write a paragraph about how you could use your talents to help others. Use at least four spelling words in your description.

_____

_____

_____

_____

_____

CA **LC 1.8** Spell correctly one-syllable words that have blends, contractions, compounds, orthographic patterns (e.g., *qu*, consonant doubling, changing the ending of a word from -*y* to -*ies* when forming the plural), and common homophones (e.g., *hair-hare*).

Name _____

> • Some **possessive pronouns** can stand alone. These include *mine*, *yours*, *his*, *hers*, *its*, *ours*, *yours*, and *theirs*.

Read the sentences and the possessive pronouns in parentheses. Write the correct possessive pronoun.

1. The students in _____ class are designing carousels.   (our, ours)

2. I am almost finished with _____.   (my, mine)

3. Did you finish _____?   (your, yours)

4. Nina and Nick showed me _____ designs.   (their, theirs)

5. Nina used dinosaurs in _____.   (her, hers)

6. Nick put only birds in _____ carousel.   (his, their)

7. I liked both of _____.   (their, theirs)

8. Each carousel had _____ own style.   (its, their)

9. _____ carousel would be different from anyone else's design.   (Your, Yours)

10. All of _____ are different.   (our, ours)

11. I hope the teacher likes _____!   (my, mine)

12. _____ class has worked really hard.   (Our, Ours)

© Macmillan/McGraw-Hill

- A **possessive pronoun** takes the place of a possessive noun. It shows who or what owns something.
- Some possessive pronouns are used before nouns. These include *my*, *your*, *his*, *her*, *its*, *our*, *your*, and *their*.
- Some possessive pronouns can stand alone. These include *mine*, *yours*, *his*, *hers*, *its*, *ours*, *yours*, and *theirs*.

Rewrite this journal entry. Be sure to correct the pronouns and nouns.

We visited ours relatives in New York City this summer. Mine cousin Tracy took we to Riverbank State Park, along the Hudson River. Her showed us an unusual carousel in the park. The octopus had two heads. The zebra was plaid. The lion was green. She explained that the carousels animals were all designed by local kids. Tracy pointed out how the artists signature is engraved beneath each animal.

_____

_____

_____

_____

_____

_____

_____

_____

_____

CA LC 1.0 Written and Oral English Language Conventions

Name _____

1. Read:

When we went on vacation, we had so much fun. We went swimming, we went shopping, we went hiking in the mountains, and we even went sailing. It was the best time ever.

2. List the four moments this student could write about:

1. _____

2. _____

3. _____

4. _____

3. Circle one moment from your list.

4. Write three more sentences about that moment.

<u>Swimming</u>: The water was cold, but I jumped in anyway. It made a big splash that soaked Dad. He jumped in and made an even bigger splash.

_____

_____

_____

_____

_____

_____

Extra Practice: Do the same activity with one of the other moments.

Every syllable in a word has only one vowel sound. When a syllable ends in a vowel, it is called an **open syllable** and usually has a long vowel sound.

Examples: ba / by   fe / male

A syllable that ends in a consonant is called a **closed syllable**. The vowel in a closed syllable usually has a short vowel sound.

Examples: sug / gest   ex / pert

Divide each underlined word into syllables. Then write whether the first syllable in each word is an open or a closed syllable.

1. Animals have traits that help them survive. _____

2. Many interesting animals live in the Southwest region of the United

States. _____

3. Some of the animals have excellent eyesight. _____

4. At night, some of the mammals hunt rodents for food.

_____

5. Certain Southwest animals can live in habitats where the temperatures

are very high. _____

6. Very large spiders live in the Southwest. _____

7. Some reptiles that live in the Southwest are poisonous.

_____

8. Some of the desert animals protect themselves in ways that are

dangerous to humans. _____

© Macmillan/McGraw-Hill

CA R 1.2 Decode regular multisyllabic words.

Name _____

A. Read the story. Then fill in the blanks with the correct words from the box.

| related to | females | identical | sight | odor | venom |

Animals may seem to be alike in many ways, but they are not

_____. Males and _____ of a

species look similar, but most females are smaller. Animals that are

_____ one another, such as dogs and wolves, are

also alike in some ways. How animals are alike is not always clear

at first _____. One way they're alike is that they

all have ways to protect themselves. Some animals spray a horrible

_____ to keep their enemies away. Others bite enemies

and _____ passes into the enemy's body.

B. Using the clues in the story, write the definitions of these vocabulary words. Check your definitions with a dictionary.

1. identical _____

2. odor _____

3. venom _____

4. sight _____

5. females _____

6. related to _____

© Macmillan/McGraw-Hill

Name _____

When you **compare and contrast** two things, you show how they are alike and how they are different. When comparing two things, look for signal words, such as *like, just as, similar, both, also,* and *too*. When contrasting two things, look for signal words, such as *different, but,* and *on the other hand*.

Read this paragraph and answer the questions below.

The desert is home to many different kinds of animals. Each of the animals has special traits that help it survive in its habitat. Reptiles, such as desert tortoises, snakes, and lizards all live in the desert Southwest. These are all cold-blooded animals, but they need different kinds of food to survive. The desert tortoise eats plants, while the snakes and lizards eat other animals. Both roadrunners and white-nosed coatis are desert animals with long tails that help them survive. The roadrunner's tail helps it balance when it runs. On the other hand, the coati's tail helps it balance in the trees it climbs.

1. In what way are all the desert animals alike? _____

_____

2. In what way are desert tortoises, snakes, and lizards alike? _____

_____

3. In what way are desert tortoises, snakes, and lizards different? _____

_____

4. How are roadrunners and white-nosed coatis alike? _____

_____

© Macmillan/McGraw-Hill

CA R 2.6 Extract appropriate and significant information from the text, including problems and solutions.

Name _____

As you read *Unique Animals of the Southwest*, fill in the Venn Diagram.

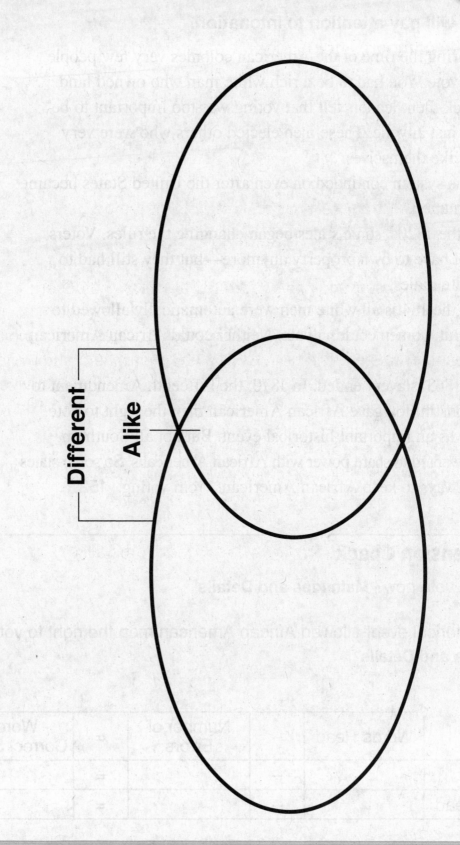

Different

Alike

How does the information you wrote in the Venn Diagram help you better understand *Unique Animals of the Southwest?*

R 2.6 Extract appropriate and significant information from the text, including problems and solutions.

As I read, I will pay attention to intonation.

	During the time of the American colonies very few people
10	could vote. You had to be a rich white man who owned land.
23	Back then, leaders felt that voting was too important to be
34	left to just anyone. These men elected others who were very
45	much like themselves.
48	This system continued on even after the United States became
58	a free nation.
61	In the 1820s, some states began changing the rules. Voters
70	did not have to own property anymore—but they still had to
82	be white males.
85	By the 1840s all white men were automatically allowed to
94	vote. But women couldn't vote. Neither could African American
103	people.
104	In 1863, slavery ended. In 1870, the Fifteenth Amendment to
112	the Constitution gave African American men the right to vote.
122	This was an important historical event. But not all Southern
132	states wanted to share power with African Americans. So some states
143	set up ways to keep African Americans from voting. 152

Comprehension Check

1. Who can vote now? **Main Idea and Details**

2. What historical event allowed African American men the right to vote?
   Main Idea and Details

	Words Read	–	Number of Errors	=	Words Correct Score
First Read		–		=	
Second Read		–		=	

© Macmillan/McGraw-Hill

CA **R 1.3** Read aloud narrative and expository text fluently and accurately and with appropriate pacing, **intonation**, and expression.

Storytellers use **foreshadowing** to give hints about what is going to happen in a story. Myths often include foreshadowing to make the story more interesting and to add suspense.

Read the passage below. Then answer the questions.

At a time long ago, Bear had a fine-looking, long, glossy tail. He thought it was the most amazing tail any animal could have. When he walked, he laid it out behind him and everybody had to walk around it. He asked everyone he met whether they thought his was the most beautiful tail they'd ever seen.

The animals, including Fox, thought Bear was very vain, but they didn't want to anger him. His giant claws and his great size and strength frightened them. So they all agreed that his big, black, shiny tail was the most beautiful they'd ever seen.

One frosty winter's day, Bear went trudging down to the stream. Fox was sitting on the ice, surrounded by fish. Fox knew that Bear was hungry.

1. What hints help you guess what will probably happen in the story?

_____

_____

2. What do you think will happen in this myth? _____

_____

_____

3. In which part of a story do you usually find foreshadowing?

_____

**Use a dictionary to find and write the part of speech and the
meaning of each word below. Then write a sentence that shows
the word's meaning.**

1. common _____

_____

_____

2. confuse _____

_____

_____

3. snatch _____

_____

_____

4. shallow _____

_____

_____

5. unique _____

_____

_____

6. dusk _____

_____

_____

© Macmillan/McGraw-Hill

CA **R 1.7** Use a dictionary to learn the meaning and other features
of unknown words.

Name _____

cozy	label	planet	spider
diner	lemon	robot	tiger
favor	model	shady	tiny
frozen	pilot	silent	

Find and Circle

Where are the spelling words?

S	P	I	D	E	R	C	O	Z	Y
Z	G	W	E	M	O	D	E	L	G
X	Q	P	O	B	B	H	J	U	T
F	N	F	C	V	O	V	F	J	I
P	L	A	N	E	T	N	T	R	G
I	A	V	T	L	Y	K	I	L	E
L	B	O	F	R	D	I	N	E	R
O	E	R	S	H	A	D	Y	M	E
T	L	S	I	L	E	N	T	O	F
U	O	P	F	R	O	Z	E	N	X

LC 1.8 Spell correctly one-syllable words that have blends, contractions, compounds, orthographic patterns (e.g., *qu*, consonant doubling, changing the ending of a word from -*y* to -*ies* when forming the plural), and common homophones (e.g., *hair-hare*).

Unique Animals of the Southwest **309**
Grade 3/Unit 5

Name _____

A. Proofreading

There are six spelling mistakes in this report. Circle the misspelled words. Write the words correctly on the lines below.

King of the Jungle

Some people think that the lion is the king of the jungle, but lions do not even live in jungles. The real king of the jungle is the tigger!

I did a report on these large cats. Here are a few things I learned. These animals live in Asia, not in Africa, as many people think. They are tiene when they are born, only two or three pounds, but they grow fast. The biggest one on the plannett weighs more than 1,000 pounds! Because they live alone, they can be siellent as they walk through the shadey forest looking for food.

The next time someone calls a lion the king of the jungle, do me a faiver, and tell them the truth!

1. _____   4. _____

2. _____   5. _____

3. _____   6. _____

B. Writing Activity

Imagine that you are an insect living in your backyard. Write a paragraph describing something about your life in this backyard home. Use at least four spelling words in your description.

_____

_____

_____

_____

_____

CA **LC 1.8** Spell correctly one-syllable words that have blends, contractions, compounds, orthographic patterns (e.g., *qu*, consonant doubling, changing the ending of a word from -*y* to -*ies* when forming the plural), and common homophones (e.g., *hair-hare*).

Name _____

- Remember, a **contraction** is a shortened form of two words. Here are some contractions:

I have = I've	I will = I'll	we will = we'll
you have = you've	he will = he'll	you will = you'll
we have = we've	she will = she'll	they will = they'll
they have = they've		

Underline the two words in each sentence that you can make into a contraction. Then write each sentence with the contraction.

1. We have seen two beavers building a home in our pond.

_____

2. It will be fun to watch them work.

_____

3. You will see them when you come over.

_____

4. I have read about beavers and their homes.

_____

5. She will find branches for their home.

_____

6. He will build with branches and mud.

_____

7. They will build an underwater door to their home.

_____

8. They have lots of building to do!

_____

© Macmillan/McGraw-Hill

- A **contraction** is a shortened form of two words.

A. Proofreading
Proofread the paragraph. Circle any incorrectly written contractions.

Im hoping to become a zoologist someday. That is someone who studies animals. Until then I can learn a lot by just watching the animals that live all around me. There are plenty of rabbits in our backyard. Theyve built their warren near our fence. Ive seen a rabbit hop across the yard. Then suddenly its gone. Its jumped down the hole into the warren. I can guess what its like inside. Its got several entrances. They lead down long tunnels. Then theyve got nests at the end of the tunnels.

B. Writing Activity
Rewrite the paragraph. Write each contraction with the apostrophe in the right place. Make sure possessive pronouns and contractions are used correctly.

_____

_____

_____

_____

_____

_____

_____

_____

CA LC 1.0 Written and Oral English Language Conventions

© Macmillan/McGraw-Hill

Name _____

1. Read:

> As I threw the ball to my dog, I heard the snow crunch as my foot slipped. My face was frozen and I could see my breath. Suddenly, a snowball hit my leg and I dove to the ground. I heard my sister laughing hysterically and could feel the cold from the snow that had gotten in my coat.

2. List the **two moments** and **two details** about each moment.

Moment 1: threw the ball

Detail: heard the snow crunch

Detail: _____

Moment 2: _____

Detail: sister laughing

Detail: _____

3. Read:

> She was sweating as she ran towards the goal line. Clouds of dust and the screams of the other players surrounded her. Launching herself into the air, she snatched the Frisbee out of the sky and landed with her arms raised victoriously. Her heart pounded and her face was a giant smile.

4. List the **two moments** and **two details** about each moment.

Moment 1: ran towards the goal line

Detail: _____

Detail: _____

Moment 2: _____

Detail: _____

Detail: _____

© Macmillan/McGraw-Hill

A **prefix** is a word part that can be added to the beginning of a base word to form a new word with a different meaning.

Prefix	Meaning	+ Base Word	New Word
dis-	not or opposite	dis + like	dislike
pre-	before or ahead of time	pre + school	preschool
un-	not or opposite	un + lucky	unlucky
re-	again	re + learn	relearn

**Read each sentence and write the correct prefix for the word.
Then write the meaning of the new word.**

1. When you _____ scramble the letters, *ipxref*, you get the word *prefix*.

   _____

2. I had to _____ organize my notes on pigs.

   _____

3. Have you ever gone to a _____ view of a children's film about animals?

   _____

4. It is important to train dogs that _____ obey commands.

   _____

5. Learning about an animal's behavior before touching it is a good

   _____ caution to take.

   _____

6. Finding a wild tiger is _____ common in the United States.

   _____

CA R 1.2 Decode regular multisyllabic words.

A. Write the vocabulary word from the box that completes each sentence below. You will need to use some words more than once.

| gaze | agreeable | guests | banquet | untrusting | curiosity |

1. The visitors and _____ at the hotel lined up for the breakfast _____.

2. Our server at dinner was pleasant and _____.

3. All the wedding _____ clapped after the bride and groom cut their cake.

4. Peanut butter is an unusual _____ in some countries, and people are afraid to try it.

5. Meat eaters are sometimes suspicious and _____ of soy burgers.

6. The tiger fixed its stare to _____ at the herd of cattle as if it were about to feast at a _____.

B. Write synonyms for the following words.

7. agreeable _____

8. curiosity _____

An **inference** is a conclusion you make about a character or an event using information or clues in the text and your own knowledge and experience. Inferences help readers understand how a plot develops.

Read the passage and make inferences by answering the questions below.

A Special Dinner

Dad and Annie went out for dinner every December 18. This year was special. Dad surprised Annie by saying, "I am taking you to a new restaurant. It serves foods from around the world."

Annie sighed. "I'm not sure about foods from other countries. I like my old favorites." Dad smiled. Annie frowned. She looked forward to this dinner and didn't want anything to go wrong.

When they arrived at the restaurant, Annie saw the sign and exclaimed, "Oh, that's what you meant by foods from around the world!" The sign said, "Grand Opening. World's Best Pizza, Tacos, and Egg Rolls!"

1. How does Annie feel about trying new things? How can you tell?

_____

_____

_____

2. How do Annie and her dad get along? How can you tell?

_____

_____

_____

© Macmillan/McGraw-Hill

Name _____

As you read *Stone Soup*, fill in the Inference Map.

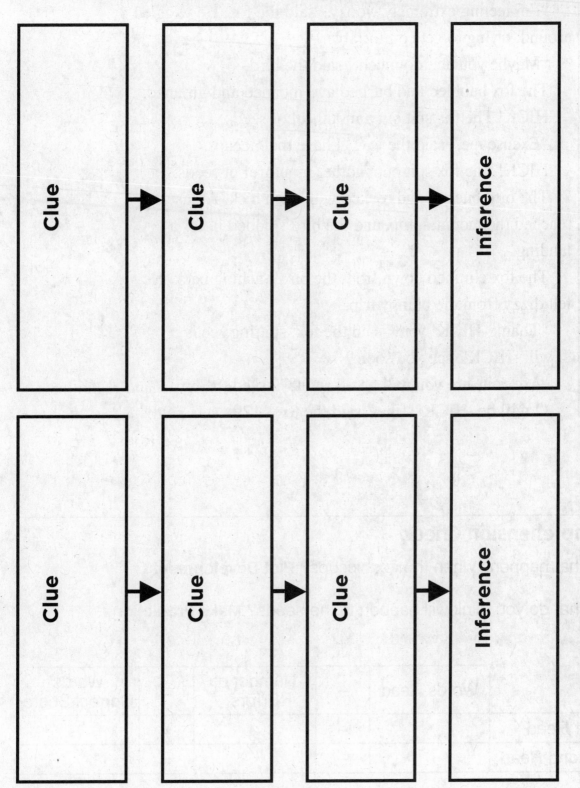

Clue → Clue → Clue → Inference

Clue → Clue → Clue → Inference

How does the information you wrote in this Inference Map help you
understand plot development in *Stone Soup*?

© Macmillan/McGraw-Hill

As I read, I will pay attention to phrasing.

	"I'm feeling extremely woozy," said the fox. He wiggled
9	around, trying to get comfortable.
14	"Maybe you ate too much," said the bird.
22	The fox bubbled and burped and moaned and groaned.
31	HICK! The fox spit out a mouthful of seeds.
40	"Excuse me," said the fox, "I have the hiccups."
49	HICK! The fox spit out another mouthful of seeds.
58	The bird bucked and rocked with each hick. At last they
69	reached the mountaintop, and the bird skidded in for a
79	landing.
80	The fox climbed down from the bird's aching back. He
90	felt dizzy from the bumpy trip.
96	"Thank -HICK! you!" said the fox, spitting seeds.
104	"I will -HICK! -see you soon."
110	"Are you sure you will be all right?" asked the bird.
121	"I will be -HICK! -fine," said the fox. 129

Comprehension Check

1. What happens when the fox hiccups? **Plot Development**

2. What do you think will happen to the seeds? **Make Predictions**

	Words Read	–	Number of Errors	=	Words Correct Score
First Read		–		=	
Second Read		–		=	

© Macmillan/McGraw-Hill

CA R 1.3 Read aloud narrative and expository text fluently and accurately and with appropriate pacing, intonation, and expression.

Name _____

Charts arrange information into columns and rows. The headings of the columns form the categories. The information in each category is arranged to help the reader compare information in categories.

Read the paragraph below. Use the information in it to fill in the missing information in the Nutritional Information for Selected Foods chart.

Eating a healthy diet means eating foods from the five different food groups: dairy, meat, fruit, breads and grains, and vegetables. You should also keep track of how many calories you consume each day. An ounce of cheddar cheese has 115 calories, and a two-ounce hamburger patty has 240 calories. Vegetables usually do not contain as many calories as breads and grains. A serving of broccoli has only 50 calories, but a bagel has 200 calories. Some fruits have very few calories, but others have many more. A serving of watermelon may have about 155 calories.

Nutritional Information for Selected Foods

Food	Food Group	Serving Size	Calories
cheddar cheese	dairy		115
hamburger	meat		240
watermelon		1 slice	
		1	200
broccoli	vegetables	1 cooked spear	

R 2.1 Use titles, tables of contents, chapter headings, glossaries, and indexes to locate information in text.

Synonyms are words that have the same, or almost the same, meaning.

Read these pairs of words that are synonyms:

happy/glad   afraid/scared   chair/seat   tool/instrument

Use a word from the box to write a synonym for the word given. Then write a sentence using both of the words.

branch	banquet	problem	cool	fast	story

1. Word: quick   Synonym: _____

Sentence: _____

_____

2. Word: twig   Synonym: _____

Sentence: _____

_____

3. Word: chilly   Synonym: _____

Sentence: _____

_____

4. Word: tired   Synonym: _____

Sentence: _____

_____

CA   R 1.4 Use knowledge of antonyms, **synonyms**, homophones, and homographs to determine the meanings of words.

© Macmillan/McGraw-Hill

Name _____

disagree	preheat	resell	untied
disappear	prepay	return	unwrap
dislike	preschool	unafraid	
precook	repay	unbeaten	

Find and Circle

Find and circle the hidden spelling words.

```
D  I  S  A  P  P  E  A  R  U
I  U  X  U  R  R  R  X  E  N
S  N  Z  N  E  E  E  D  P  A
A  T  K  W  P  S  T  I  R  F
G  I  Q  R  A  C  U  S  I  R
R  E  P  A  Y  H  R  L  N  A
E  D  Q  P  Z  O  N  I  T  I
E  P  R  E  C  O  O  K  Q  D
R  E  S  E  L  L  K  E  X  Z
U  N  B  E  A  T  E  N  Z  K
K  X  P  R  E  H  E  A  T  Z
```

CA LC 1.8 Spell correctly one-syllable words that have blends,
contractions, compounds, orthographic patterns (e.g., *qu*, consonant
doubling, changing the ending of a word from *-y* to *-ies* when forming
the plural), and common homophones (e.g., *hair-hare*).

Stone Soup • Grade 3/Unit 6   **321**

Name _____

A. There are six spelling mistakes in this paragraph. Circle the misspelled words. Write the words correctly on the lines below.

My sister Ariel is in preskoul. She has a cat named Sally. Ariel and Sally both disslike dogs. They run screaming if they see a dog, no matter how gentle or sweet the dog is.

One day, Ariel and I were in the yard playing when we heard a dog barking near our house. I was unafrade, so I went to see why he was barking. When I got closer, I saw Sally tangled in the dog's leash. She was scratching at him, but he was just sitting there calling for help. When I untyed the cat, the dog ran off.

Ariel would like to reepay the dog for his kindness, but we have never seen him rettern.

1. _____   4. _____

2. _____   5. _____

3. _____   6. _____

B. Writing Activity

Do you have a pet? Is there an animal you would like to have for a pet? Write a paragraph describing your pet or the pet you would like to have. Use at least four spelling words in your description.

_____

_____

_____

_____

_____

CA **LC 1.8** Spell correctly one-syllable words that have blends, contractions, compounds, orthographic patterns (e.g., *qu*, consonant doubling, changing the ending of a word from *-y* to *-ies* when forming the plural), and common homophones (e.g., *hair-hare*).

Name _____

- An **adjective** tells *what kind* or *how many*.
- Use the **articles** *a* and *an* before singular nouns. Use *a* before a word that starts with a consonant. Use *an* before a word that starts with a vowel.
- Use *the* before a singular or plural noun.

Complete each sentence with an adjective from the box. Some adjectives may be used more than once.

an	one	the	magic	strange	tall
tiny	two	a	beautiful	new	

1. My brothers and I share _____ room.

2. Our _____ apartment doesn't have much space.

3. I like to look at _____ houses while walking to school.

4. One _____ house always catches my attention.

5. It has a _____ tower on one corner.

6. The house looks like a _____ castle.

7. It is _____ unusual sight on our street.

8. I think about living in _____ castle like that.

9. Our room has _____ windows.

10. One house has a _____ garden.

11. We helped by putting _____ shelf up.

12. There is a _____ rug on the floor.

© Macmillan/McGraw-Hill

CA **LC 1.2** Identify subjects and verbs that are in agreement and identify and use pronouns, adjectives, compound words, and articles correctly in writing and speaking.

- An **adjective** tells *what kind* or *how many*.
- Use the **articles** *a* and *an* before singular nouns. Use *a* before a word starting with a consonant. Use *an* before a word starting with a vowel.
- Use *the* before a singular or plural noun.

A. Proofread the paragraph. Underline the adjectives. Circle any articles that are used incorrectly.

No one had lived in an old house on Cray Street for a long time. It was in bad shape. Windows were broken. The porch sagged. A wall had fallen down inside. Then a community group bought the house. They were going to fix it and give it to an family in town. I helped clean up the rooms. I carried materials to a carpenters. I learned how to measure and cut wood. Best of all, I got to pick out colors for a rooms! Everyone loves the new living room and dining room that I painted.

B. Rewrite the paragraph. Write the articles correctly. Add any adjectives that will make the paragraph better.

_____

_____

_____

_____

_____

_____

_____

CA **LC 1.2** Identify subjects and verbs that are in agreement and identify and use pronouns, adjectives, compound words, and articles correctly in writing and speaking.

Name _____

Practice

Writing:
Character
Development:
Believable

1. **Brainstorm** three things you did yesterday or today. These should be things you think other kids your age do sometimes too.

> **Example:** *ate a snack*

> 1.

> 2.

> 3.

2. **Circle** one of the moments from your brainstorm.

3. **Think** about the moment you circled.

4. **List** three things you did or said in the moment you circled.

> **Example:** *asked Mom for another cookie*

> 1.

> 2.

> 3.

5. **Write** three to five sentences about a made-up kid doing the activity you described. What does the kid do and say in that moment?

_____

_____

_____

_____

_____

_____

In two-syllable words with a final unstressed syllable ending in
-**el** or -**le**, the final vowel sound is usually the sound you hear in
angel and *bottle*.
• When two or more consonants come between two vowels,
the syllables are usually divided between the consonants, as
in *shut / tle.*
• When a single consonant comes between two vowels, the
word is usually divided after the consonant, as in *mod / el.*
• It is divided before the consonant if the vowel sound is long,
as in *la / bel.*

**Fill in the blank with a word from the box. Then write the word
again, showing how it is divided into syllables.**

travel   pickle   riddle   stall   shovel   hall   simple   little

1. I like to _____ to different states. _____

2. My new bedroom is not as _____ as my old bedroom.

   _____

3. Every time my uncle visits, he tells me a _____.

   _____

4. In the winter, I always have to _____ the snow off the

   sidewalk. _____

5. I like to put a _____ on my sandwich. _____

6. Luckily, picking out a color to paint my bedroom walls was

   _____. _____

CA R 1.2 Decode regular multisyllabic words.

A. Read the sentences. Fill in the blanks with the correct words from the box.

| securing | decorated | weakest | darkened | symbol | gnaws |

1. Jim wanted to make the stage prettier, so he _____ it with flowers.

2. Megan drew a picture of a dove on the cover of the program. She said

   that it was a _____ that stood for peace.

3. At the end of the play, the stage was _____ so there wasn't as much light as there was at the beginning.

4. Some of the costumes have holes in them. The stagehands think a

   mouse _____ on them at night.

5. The guards are _____ the theater by locking the doors to make it safe.

6. The _____ stage helper has the least amount of strength to lift the stage props.

B. Write new sentences for two of the vocabulary words used above. Then underline the vocabulary word.

7. _____

   _____

8. _____

   _____

When you **summarize** a story or selection, you write the most important information or main idea.

Read each paragraph below. Then write a summary.

1. Last night was the final performance of the school play. The theater was packed. Every seat was taken. The play went on without any problems. In the end, the audience stood up and clapped. They all agreed it was the best play they had ever seen.

Summary: _____

_____

_____

2. A new movie with Ray's favorite superhero was coming to the theater. He did not have enough money to go. He really wanted to see this movie. Ray decided he would earn the money. He washed his dad's car. He cleaned his sister's room, and he put away his mom's clothes for her. By the time the movie got to the theater, Ray had enough money to see the movie and have some popcorn!

Summary: _____

_____

_____

CA R 2.5 Distinguish the main idea and supporting details in expository text.

Name _____

As you read *The Strongest One*, fill in the Story Map.

Character

Setting

Beginning

↓

Middle

↓

End

How does the information you wrote in this Story Map help you
summarize *The Strongest One*?

CA **R 2.5** Distinguish the main idea and supporting details in
expository text.

The Strongest One • **Grade 3/Unit 6** **329**

Name _____

As I read, I will pay attention to expression and intonation.

	Narrator: One evening, when John was out in the
9	woods digging up the roots of an old tree for King George,
21	his shovel hit something hard.
26	**John:** What's this? An old trunk with a mysterious
35	symbol on it! Oh goodness, it's a pile of gold coins—really
47	buried treasure!
49	**Narrator:** John danced for joy, but then he realized he
59	had a big problem.
63	**John:** If the king finds out about this treasure, he will
74	keep all of it. If I tell Maria about it, she will tell the whole
89	world.
90	**Narrator:** John thought of a plan to fool the king and
101	keep the treasure for the villagers. 107

Comprehension Check

1. What is John's problem? **Problem and Solution**

2. Why does John want to keep the treasure a secret? **Plot**

	Words Read	–	Number of Errors	=	Words Correct Score
First Read		–		=	
Second Read		–		=	

© Macmillan/McGraw-Hill

 R 1.3 Read aloud narrative and expository text fluently and accurately and with appropriate pacing, intonation, and expression.

A **diagram** is a drawing that explains information. Some information is easier to understand by looking at a diagram than by reading about it.

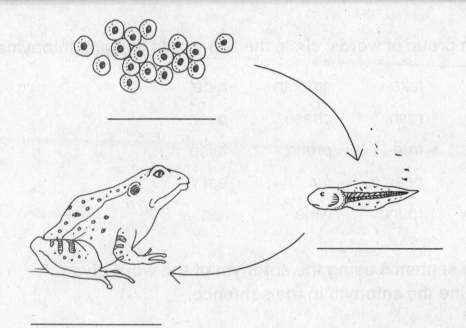

_____

_____

_____

Use these terms to answer the questions below. Then write the words in the diagram.

tadpole	eggs	frog	Life Cycle of a Frog

1. What does the diagram show? _____

2. What is the first part of the life cycle? _____

3. What is the name of the adult animal? _____

4. What is the name of the animal in the middle of the life cycle?

_____

© Macmillan/McGraw-Hill

CA **R 2.1** Use titles, tables of contents, chapter headings, glossaries, and dictionaries to locate information in text.

The Strongest One • Grade 3/Unit 6   **331**

Name _____

> **Antonyms** are words that have opposite meanings. Read the examples of antonym pairs:
>
> soft/hard   dark/light   fast/slow   happy/sad

A. In each group of words, circle the two words that are antonyms.

1. rough   take   smooth   hide
2. pull   rush   chase   push
3. gray   true   proud   false
4. strike   near   far   eat
5. narrow   round   wide   red

B. Write a sentence using the antonym of the word given.
Underline the antonym in the sentence.

6. weakest _____

_____

7. awake _____

_____

8. clean _____

_____

9. high _____

_____

10. cry _____

_____

© Macmillan/McGraw-Hill

CA   **R 1.4** Use knowledge of **antonyms**, synonyms, homophones, and homographs to determine the meanings of words.

Name _____

Practice

Spelling:
Words with
Consonant + *le*
Syllables

Using the Word Study Steps

1. LOOK at the word.

2. SAY the word aloud.

3. STUDY the letters in the word.

4. WRITE the word.

5. CHECK the word.
   Did you spell the word right?
   If not, go back to step 1.

A. Rhyme Time

Circle the word in each row that rhymes with the word on the left.

1. tickle	ticket	pickle	picnic
2. table	able	bubble	trouble
3. middle	rattle	puddle	riddle
4. owl	towel	bowl	town
5. pickle	picking	nickel	nibble
6. candle	handy	handsome	handle

B. X the Word

Put an X on the word that does not fit the pattern in each row.

7. little	puzzle	barrel	riddle
8. pickle	panel	purple	puzzle
9. travel	tunnel	towel	handle
10. castle	camel	cattle	couple
11. awful	able	eagle	table
12. handle	stable	sparkle	squirrel

© Macmillan/McGraw-Hill

LC 1.8 Spell correctly one-syllable words that have blends,
contractions, compounds, orthographic patterns (e.g., *qu*, consonant
doubling, changing the ending of a word from -*y* to -*ies* when forming
the plural), and common homophones (e.g., *hair-hare*).

The Strongest One • **Grade 3/Unit 6**   **333**

Name _____

A. There are six spelling mistakes in this paragraph. Circle the misspelled words. Write the words correctly on the lines below.

My parents always taught me that it is important to give to those who have less than we do. It does not have to mean giving money. If you are abbel, it is also great to give your time and talents.

Each summer, we travle to a nearby city and work with a group of people building a house for another family. Even when I was litel, I could help by passing out lunch to the workers. Everyone got a sandwich and a pikkel. Then I would spend the afternoon playing with toys or a puzle with other kids.

Last year, I was old enough to handel a bigger job. I would bring the right tools to my mom and dad.

It feels good to help others. It can be a lot of fun, too!

1. _____   4. _____

2. _____   5. _____

3. _____   6. _____

B. Writing Activity

Do you have a hero? People who help others are community heroes. Write four questions you would like to ask your hero. Use at least three spelling words in your questions.

_____

_____

_____

_____

_____

_____

LC 1.8 Spell correctly one-syllable words that have blends, contractions, compounds, orthographic patterns (e.g., *qu*, consonant doubling, changing the ending of a word from -*y* to -*ies* when forming the plural), and common homophones (e.g., *hair-hare*).

Name _____

- If an adjective ends in a consonant and **y**, change the **y** to **i** before adding **-er** or **-est**.
- If an adjective ends in **e**, drop the **e** before adding **-er** or **-est**.
- If an adjective has a single vowel before a final consonant, double the final consonant before adding **-er** or **-est**.

Change y to i:	happy	happier	happiest
Drop the e:	safe	safer	safest
Double the consonant:	hot	hotter	hottest

A. Add -er or -est to each adjective. Write the correct form.

Add -er

1. pretty _____
2. blue _____
3. big _____
4. noisy _____
5. red _____

Add -est

6. white _____
7. tiny _____
8. pale _____
9. fat _____
10. silly _____

B. Write the correct form of each adjective in parentheses.

11. Charlotte was the (nice) _____ spider anyone knew.

12. The (busy) _____ worker in the barn was Charlotte.

13. Templeton was (lazy) _____ than Wilbur.

14. It was the (wet) _____ day anyone had ever seen.

15. The fair was the (happy) _____ day of Wilbur's life.

© Macmillan/McGraw-Hill

Name _____

- Add **-er** to an adjective to compare two nouns and **-est** to compare more than two nouns.
- If an adjective ends in a consonant and **y**, change the **y** to **i** before adding **-er** or **-est**.
- If an adjective ends in **e**, drop the **e** before adding **-er** or **-est**.
- If an adjective has a single vowel before a final consonant, double the final consonant before adding **-er** or **-est**.

A. Proofread these lines of dialogue. Circle any adjectives that are incorrectly used or misspelled.

"I remember the scaryiest thing that ever happened to me. I woke up before dawn and couldn't go back to sleep. I turned on the kitchen light and walked through the door. Suddenly, there was something on my face—the biggest, gummyest spiderweb I had ever seen! I let out the louddest scream I had ever screamed. Then I started to laugh. After all, what was sillyer than getting upset about a spiderweb?"

B. Rewrite the dialogue. Write the comparative adjectives correctly.

_____

_____

_____

_____

_____

_____

© Macmillan/McGraw-Hill

CA LC 1.0 Written and Oral English Language Conventions

Name _____

1. Read:

*Mira couldn't believe her eyes. It was the funniest thing she had
ever seen!*

2. Write two or three more sentences that show what Mira saw and how
she reacted in this moment.

_____

_____

_____

_____

_____

_____

_____

_____

_____

_____

_____

_____

_____

© Macmillan/McGraw-Hill

CA W 1.0 Writing Strategies

Every syllable in a word has only one vowel sound. When two vowels come together and stand for one vowel sound, they form a vowel team. That vowel sound is usually long. A vowel team stays in the same syllable. A syllable that has a vowel team is called a **vowel team syllable.**
Examples: **soak**/ing, **teach**/er, **rain**/y

Divide each underlined word into syllables. Then write the vowel team syllable.

1. <u>People</u> like to listen to storytellers. _____

2. They like <u>stories</u> about tricksters. _____

3. Trickster tales were used for <u>teaching</u> lessons. _____

4. They help <u>explain</u> why things happen in nature. _____

5. Most trickster tales are <u>about</u> animals. _____

6. Many trickster tales have animals that live in the <u>Southwest</u> as

   characters. _____

7. People <u>enjoy</u> hearing about how one animal tricks another.

   _____

8. I always carry a book of trickster tales in my <u>bookbag</u>.

   _____

CA R 1.2 Decode regular multisyllabic words.

Name _____

A. Read the story. Then fill in each blank with the correct word from the box.

| insightful | technique | majority | investigate | cunning |

A _____ of people love listening to trickster

tales. These tales are _____ stories that help people

think about things in new ways. Each storyteller uses a different

_____ to tell a trickster tale. The characters are often

amusing, and very often the main character is _____.

After hearing a trickster tale, people may _____ to find

other stories in which the same lesson is taught.

B. Using clues in the story, write the definitions of these vocabulary words. Check your definitions by using a dictionary.

6. insightful _____

_____

7. technique _____

8. majority _____

9. investigate _____

_____

10. cunning _____

When you **compare and contrast** two things, you show how they are alike and how they are different.

When you compare, use signal words such as *like*, *just as*, *similar*, *both*, *also*, and *too*. When you contrast, use signal words such as *different*, *but*, *while*, and *on the other hand*.

Read this paragraph, and answer the questions below.

Trickster tales are all folk tales. They all include characters that are very clever. In these stories, a smaller animal often outwits a larger, more powerful animal. Some trickster tales teach lessons that are important for people to know, while others explain how and why things happen in nature. But in different cultures, the story characters may be different. The trickster may be a different animal or have a different body.

1. How are all trickster tales alike? _____

_____

_____

2. How are trickster tales different from one another? _____

_____

_____

3. How are trickster story characters different in various cultures?

_____

_____

4. What signal words tell you that the passage is comparing and

contrasting? _____

(CA)   **R 2.6** Extract appropriate and significant information from the text, including problems and solutions.

© Macmillan/McGraw-Hill

Name _____

As you read Tales of the Trickster, fill in the Venn Diagram.

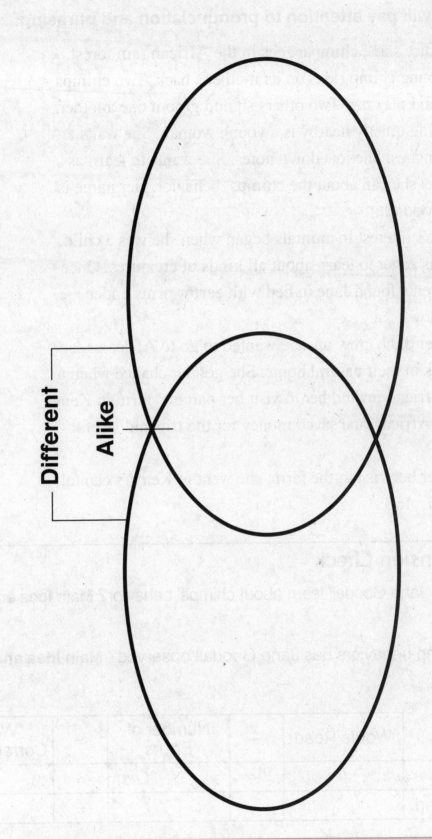

Different

Alike

How does the information you wrote in the Venn Diagram help you better understand Tales of the Trickster?

R 2.6 Extract appropriate and significant information from the text, including problems and solutions.

Tales of the Trickster
Grade 3/Unit 6   **341**

As I read, I will pay attention to pronunciation and phrasing.

	Picture some chimpanzees in the African rain forest.
8	One young chimp rides on its mother's back. Two chimps
18	romp and play tag. Two others sit and groom one another.
29	Sitting quietly nearby is a young woman. She waits.
38	She watches. She jots down notes. She wants to learn as
49	much as she can about the chimps' behavior. Her name is
60	Jane Goodall.
62	Jane's interest in animals began when she was a child.
72	She was eager to learn about all kinds of creatures. Once
83	her parents found Jane in bed with earthworms under
92	her pillow!
94	When Jane grew up, she wanted to go to Africa to see
106	animals in their natural home. She got her chance when a
117	school friend invited her to visit her parents' farm in Kenya
128	in east Africa. Jane saved money for the trip and left for
140	Africa.
141	After her visit to the farm, she went to Kenya's capital,
152	Nairobi. 153

Comprehension Check

1. How does Jane Goodall learn about chimps' behavior? **Main Idea and Details**

2. What chimp behaviors has Jane Goodall observed? **Main Idea and Details**

	Words Read	−	Number of Errors	=	Words Correct Score
First Read		−		=	
Second Read		−		=	

CA **R 1.3** Read aloud narrative and expository text fluently and accurately and with appropriate pacing, intonation, and expression.

A **functional document** gives people information or helps
them know how to do something.
  • Forms, menus, advertisements, pamphlets, and brochures
    give information and help us do things.
  • Flyers, posters, and schedules are handed out or put in
    public places to announce the times, places, and dates that
    an event will take place.

Imagine that your class is having a bake sale to raise money for the field trip to
the museum in the city. Informing a lot of people is a good way to raise money.

Answer the questions below about the bake sale.

1. What do you think is the best way to advertise the bake sale? Why?

_____

_____

2. Where do you think are good places to hang posters?

_____

_____

3. What information would you include on your functional document?

_____

_____

4. What kinds of events have you seen advertised on functional documents?

_____

_____

© Macmillan/McGraw-Hill

Compare/Contrast Writing Frame

A. Summarize *Tales of the Trickster*. Use the Compare/Contrast Writing Frame below.

Both Robert Greygrass and Rose Red Elk are the **same** in some ways. They are the same because _____

_____

_____.

However, in other ways Robert Greygrass and Rose Red Elk are **different**. They are different because _____

_____

_____.

So, Robert Greygrass and Rose Red Elk have both **similarities and differences**.

B. Rewrite the completed summary on another sheet of paper. Keep it as a model for writing a summary of an article or selection using this text structure.

© Macmillan/McGraw-Hill

CA R 2.0 Reading Comprehension

Prefixes are word parts that can be added to the beginning of base words to form new words with new meanings.

Prefix	Meaning	Example
re-	to do again	retell
un-	not or opposite	uneven
dis-	not or opposite	disconnect

Suffixes are word parts that can be added to the end of base words to form new words with new meanings.

Suffix	Meaning	Example
-ful	full of, tending to	useful
-ly	in a certain manner or way, like	quickly
-er	someone who does	singer

Write the word in each sentence that includes a prefix or a suffix. Then write the meaning of the word.

1. People love to listen to playful stories about tricksters. _____

    Meaning: _____

2. Trickster tales often make people laugh and are never uninteresting.

    _____

    Meaning: _____

3. Few people disagree with the lessons in trickster tales. _____

    Meaning: _____

4. Every listener can learn something important from the tales.

    _____

    Meaning: _____

© Macmillan/McGraw-Hill

 R 1.8 Use knowledge of prefixes (e.g., *un-*, *re-*, *pre-*, *bi-*, *mis-*, *dis-*) and suffixes (e.g., *-er*, *-est*, *-ful*) to determine the meaning of words.

Tales of the Trickster **345**
Grade 3/Unit 6

Use the Word Study Steps.

1. LOOK at the word.

2. SAY the word.

3. STUDY the word.

4. WRITE the word.

5. CHECK the word.

Did you spell the word right?
If not, go back to step 1.

A. Circle the word in each row that rhymes with the word in dark type.

1. complain	complete	contain	certain
2. remain	remind	unclean	obtain
3. detail	decal	retail	destroy
4. coffee	clearly	crafty	toffee
5. repeat	repair	defeat	rebate
6. about	above	coach	without
7. reading	bedding	leading	treading
8. appear	approach	unclear	appeal
9. enjoyed	annoyed	entered	repaired
10. unreal	unwrap	appeal	unread

B. The answer to each riddle is a word with a vowel team syllable. Write the word on the line.

11. I name something that can kill living things. My first syllable rhymes with *boy*, but isn't spelled the same way. _____

12. I mean "hard to see or understand." I start with a prefix that means "not," and I rhyme with *severe*. _____

CA **LC 1.8** Spell correctly one-syllable words that have blends, contractions, compounds, orthographic patterns (e.g., *qu*, consonant doubling, changing the ending of a word from *-y* to *-ies* when forming the plural) and common homophones (e.g., *hair-hare*).

Name _____

A. There are six spelling mistakes in this paragraph. Circle the misspelled words. Write the words correctly on the lines below.

Tales Retold

People in countries all over the world have enjoid trickster tales for many years. Storytellers repeete them over and over. Stories abuot tricksters are often amusing. The purpose of some trickster tales is explayning how things work in nature. When raeding a trickster tale, you expect the trickster to do something clever. In some trickster tales, it may appare that the trickster will outwit another character, but instead the trickster gets tricked!

1. _____   4. _____

2. _____   5. _____

3. _____   6. _____

B. Write a paragraph about trickster tales. Use at least three spelling words in your paragraph.

_____

_____

_____

_____

_____

_____

_____

© Macmillan/McGraw-Hill

CA **LC 1.8** Spell correctly one-syllable words that have blends, contractions, compounds, orthographic patterns (e.g., *qu*, consonant doubling, changing the ending of a word from -*y* to -*ies* when forming the plural) and common homophones (e.g., *hair-hare*).

Name _____

• **Adverbs** can be put in different places in a sentence. Moving an adverb may make the sentence sound better.
    People **eagerly** follow space missions.
    People follow space missions **eagerly**.

Add -ly to the adjective in parentheses to form an adverb. Write the sentence, placing the adverb where you think it sounds best.

1. (swift) The shuttle launches.

_____

2. (wild) The crowd cheers.

_____

3. (immediate) The astronauts get to work.

_____

4. (careful) John Glenn checks his heartbeat.

_____

5. (eager) The scientists follow his progress.

_____

6. (great) They are excited about the experiments.

_____

7. (automatic) Some of the shuttle's systems run.

_____

8. (perfect) The shuttle runs itself.

_____

CA LC 1.0 Written and Oral English Language Conventions

Name _____

- An **adverb** is a word that tells more about a verb.
- Most adverbs that tell *how* end in **-ly**. They are formed by adding **-ly** to an adjective.

A. Proofread the paragraph. Circle any adverbs that are incorrect or in the wrong place.

   I made my own space shuttle for a science project. I worked endless on it! First, I careful drew a design. Then I measured and cut out pieces of cardboard. The pieces had to fit together perfect. I was sad when some didn't fit exact. But I just went back and tried again. This time everything slid easy into place. I used tape to hold it together secure. Then I painted neatly some small details onto it. I gentle added a string. Then I pulled it rapid through the air. It real looked like it was flying!

B. Rewrite the paragraph. Write the adverbs correctly.

_____

_____

_____

_____

_____

_____

_____

_____

_____

_____

Writing Rubric			
4 Excellent	3 Good	2 Fair	1 Unsatisfactory
Ideas and Content/Genre	Ideas and Content/Genre	Ideas and Content/Genre	Ideas and Content/Genre
Organization and Focus	Organization and Focus	Organization and Focus	Organization and Focus
Sentence Structure/ Fluency	Sentence Structure/ Fluency	Sentence Structure/ Fluency	Sentence Structure/ Fluency
Conventions	Conventions	Conventions	Conventions
Word Choice	Word Choice	Word Choice	Word Choice
Voice	Voice	Voice	Voice
Presentation	Presentation	Presentation	Presentation

CA W 1.0 Writing Strategies

Name _____

When **er**, **ar**, or **or** come at the end of a final unstressed syllable, it stands for the /ər/ sound, as in *writer*, *cellar*, and *sailor*.

---

brother	mayor	voter	uncle	November	singer	nickel
trailer	editor	sailor	dollar	handle	April	

A. Fill in each blank with a word from the box that has the final /ər/ sound.

1. The election was held during the first week of _____.

2. Each _____ made sure to cast a vote before the polls closed.

3. There was big turnout to elect a _____ for the city.

4. My _____ wrote a letter to the newspaper encouraging everyone to vote.

5. He also suggested that every voter should give a _____ to the candidates' favorite charity.

6. The jazz _____ donated the fee for her performance to the food bank.

B. Use the following /ər/ words in a sentence.

7. sailor: _____

_____

8. editor: _____

_____

Name _____

A. Write the vocabulary word that best completes each sentence below.

recipes   magnificent   ingredient
tasty   masterpiece   tradition

1. José read many _____ until he found the best one for chocolate cake.

2. He planned to bake the most _____ cake ever for his grandmother's birthday.

3. The only missing _____ was the chocolate!

4. Chocolate would make the cake very _____.

5. José put the finished cake on the counter. It looked like a

_____.

6. We decided that making chocolate birthday cakes should be a family

_____.

B. Write the definitions for two of the vocabulary words.

7. _____

_____

8. _____

_____

CA R 1.0 Word Analysis, Fluency, and Systematic Vocabulary Development

When you **compare and contrast** things, you look at the characteristics of each thing and point out how they are alike and how they are different.

Read the following paragraph, and answer the questions below.

George the rooster and Jen the chicken have been friends for many years. They both love being in the kitchen, but George likes to bake cookies and Jen likes to bake pies. Jen makes her pies with different types of fruit, and George makes his cookies with different nuts and chips. Both the cookies and pies are very tasty. Because everyone likes their cookies and pies, George and Jen decided to open a bakery so everyone could try them. George sells his cookies by the pound, and Jen sells her pies one at a time. Both of them sold everything on their first day.

1. Compare George and Jen. Tell how they are alike.

_____

_____

_____

_____

2. Contrast George and Jen. Tell how they are different.

_____

_____

_____

_____

© Macmillan/McGraw-Hill

As you read *Cook-a-Doodle-Doo!*, fill in the Venn Diagram.

Rooster   **Both**   **Little Red Hen**

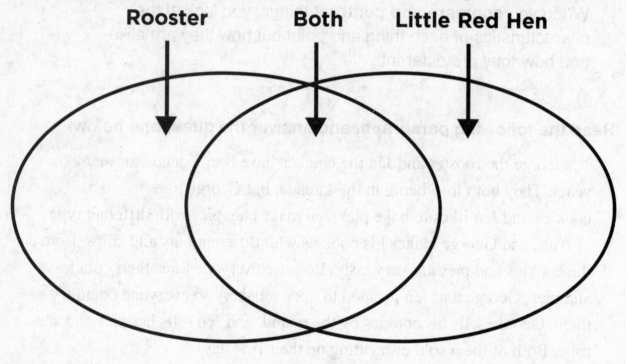

Pig   **Both**   **Turtle**

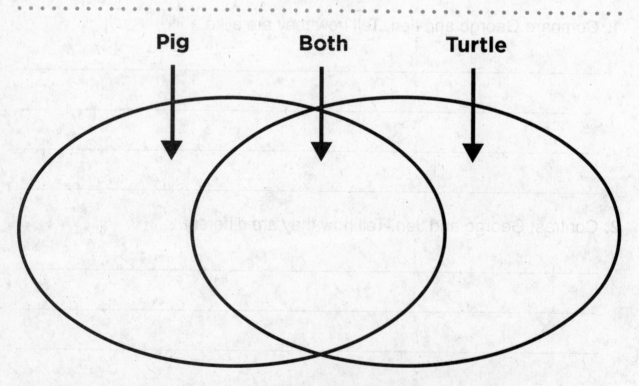

How does the information you wrote in this Venn Diagram help you compare and contrast characters in *Cook-a-Doodle-Doo!*?

CA **R 2.0** Reading Comprehension

As I read, I will pay attention to phrasing.

	Even kids can be inventors. Frank Epperson was 11
8	years old when he proved it! One night, he mixed powdered
19	fruit flavor in a cup of soda water. He stirred it with a stick.
33	That's how people made fruit drinks in 1905. But after a
43	sip or two, Frank left his drink on the back porch.
54	The night grew very cold. By morning, Frank had a
64	magnificent surprise. His fruit soda had frozen to the stick.
74	Frank showed it to his friends. At first everyone thought
84	Frank had lost his marbles. They thought he was crazy.
94	But after one lick, everyone cheered. Frank's invention was
103	a masterpiece. A work of art! Frank called it an Epsicle.
114	Frank decided to sell the icy treats. 121

Comprehension Check

1. How was a fruit drink made in 1905? **Main Idea and Details**

2. How did Frank Epperson discover popsicles? **Main Idea and Details**

	Words Read	–	Number of Errors	=	Words Correct Score
First Read		–		=	
Second Read		–		=	

© Macmillan/McGraw-Hill

CA R 1.3 Read aloud narrative and expository text fluently and accurately
and with appropriate pacing, intonation, and expression.

Cock-a-Doodle-Doo! **355**
Grade 3/Unit 6

A **diagram** explains information by using words and drawings. Some information is easier to understand by looking at a diagram than by reading about it.

All the food that you eat needs to be digested. Look at the diagram that shows how food is digested. Use these words to help you answer the questions.

mouth   esophagus   stomach   pancreas   liver   intestine

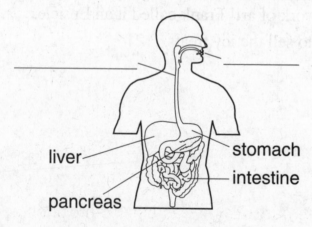

liver

stomach

intestine

pancreas

1. What would be a good title for this diagram? _____

2. On the correct line in the diagram, label the body part you use to chew food. _____

3. On the correct line in the diagram, label the body part that leads to the stomach. _____

4. The pancreas makes juices that help you digest food. Which body part is nearest the pancreas? _____

© Macmillan/McGraw-Hill

CA **R 2.1** Use titles, tables of contents, chapter headings, glossaries, and indexes to locate information in text.

An **idiom** is a phrase with a meaning that is different from the meaning of each word in it.

Authors use these special words or phrases to make their language more colorful. To figure out the meaning of an idiom, read the sentence carefully to understand how it is used.

A. Circle the idiom in each sentence below. Write the meaning of the idiom on the next line.

1. Both Dad and Mom work hard to bring home the bacon.

_____

2. Hitting a home run was a piece of cake for our best batter.

_____

3. She had to use her noodle to figure out how to fix the bike.

_____

4. Sam is the big cheese because he was elected president.

_____

5. That's the recipe in a nutshell!.

_____

B. Write a sentence using one idiom from above.

6. _____

_____

Using the Word Study Steps

1. LOOK at the word.

2. SAY the word aloud.

3. STUDY the letters in the word.

4. WRITE the word.

5. CHECK the word.
   Did you spell the word right?
   If not, go back to step 1.

A. Rhyme Time

Circle the word in each row that rhymes with the word on the left.

1. player	layer	flyer	platter
2. trailer	silver	sailing	sailor
3. fighter	writer	water	fatter
4. collar	color	dollar	deliver
5. answer	drawer	dancer	dinner
6. mister	sister	master	clowns

B. X the Word

Put an X on the word that does not fit the pattern in each row.

7. sister	silver	summer	sailor
8. December	dancer	doctor	danger
9. tractor	trailer	toaster	temper
10. cellar	dollar	duller	collar
11. winter	visitor	writer	layer
12. matter	author	mayor	anchor

© Macmillan/McGraw-Hill

(CA) **LC 1.8** Spell correctly one-syllable words that have blends, contractions, compounds, orthographic patterns (e.g., *qu*, consonant doubling, changing the ending of a word from -*y* to -*ies* when forming the plural), and common homophones (e.g., *hair-hare*).

Name _____

A. There are six spelling mistakes in this speech. Circle the misspelled words. Write the words correctly on the lines below.

Hello, my fellow citizens. Thank you so much for coming out on this cold winnter day. Seeing you all here is very inspiring. Running for mayur has been a great experience. I have met so many people in this community. Yesterday, I spoke to a docter who is concerned about our hospitals. Later, I spoke to a sailer who is afraid our ports are too crowded. I even spoke to a danser who says there is not enough appreciation for the arts. With your help, we will win the election in Decembur. Then I can help everyone with these issues.

I'll see you on election day!

1. _____   4. _____

2. _____   5. _____

3. _____   6. _____

B. Writing Activity

Pretend you are running for class president. Write a speech you would give to your class. Use at least three spelling words in your paragraph.

_____

_____

_____

_____

_____

_____

LC 1.8 Spell correctly one-syllable words that have blends, contractions, compounds, orthographic patterns (e.g., *qu*, consonant doubling, changing the ending of a word from -*y* to -*ies* when forming the plural), and common homophones (e.g., *hair-hare*).

Cock-a-Doodle-Doo!   **359**
Grade 3/Unit 6

- Some **adverbs** tell where an action takes place.
- Adverbs that tell *where* include *there*, *outside*, *up*, *here*, *nearby*, *ahead*, *around*, *far*, *away*, and *everywhere*.

Draw one line under each adverb that tells *where*. Draw two lines under the verb it describes.

1. The baby tigers didn't live outside.

2. They stayed here, inside the apartment.

3. The tigers roamed everywhere in the apartment.

4. They didn't go far from Helen, though.

5. She stayed nearby and watched them.

6. Dacca saw the curtains and climbed up.

7. Rajpur crawled around the sofa.

8. Raniganj jumped ahead of the others.

9. Finally, the tigers went away to the zoo.

10. With some help, Helen and Fred moved the tigers there.

11. They do not always like being inside.

12. I have been here before.

13. The tigers went everywhere with them.

14. The zoo was not far from my school.

15. We walked around the zoo.

CA **LC 1.0** Written and Oral English Language Conventions

Name _____

- Some **adverbs** tell *when* an action takes place.
- Some adverbs tell *where* an action takes place.

A. Proofread the passage. Circle adverbs that tell *when* or *where*.

Today we met a zookeeper. Yes her name is Meg. Early in the day, she gave us a tour of the zoo. First we went outside. There we saw the workers feed the animals. Ahead we saw a sign for the nursery. We came inside. Here is where the zoo takes care of the baby tigers. Two baby tigers just arrived yesterday. They are awake now. It is fun to see them close to us. Wow it's late. Therefore we must go home soon. However tomorrow I will look for books about baby tigers.

B. Writing Activity

Rewrite the paragraph. Add commas after introductory words.

_____

_____

_____

_____

_____

_____

_____

_____

_____

Name _____

Practice

Writing:
Character Development:
Shows Change and
Growth

1. **Think** of a thing or activity that you **didn't** like before, but **do** like now.

2. **Write** the name of that thing or activity.

_____

3. **Write** two to three sentences about when you **didn't** like it. What did you do or say?

_____

_____

_____

_____

_____

4. **Write** two to three sentences that show what you do or say now that you **do** like it.

_____

_____

_____

_____

_____

_____

_____

_____

_____

_____

_____

CA W 1.0 Writing Strategies

© Macmillan/McGraw-Hill

Suffixes are word parts that can be added to the end of words. Adding a suffix forms a new word with a new meaning.

Suffix	Meaning	Example
-ful	full of, tending to	useful
-less	not having, without	sleepless
-ly	in a certain manner or way, like	mostly

Below each sentence, write the word that includes a suffix. Then write the meaning of the word.

1. Mrs. Linwood is always very cheerful when I bring my puppy over to play.

_____

Meaning: _____

2. Newborn puppies and kittens are helpless without their mothers.

_____

Meaning: _____

3. Standing in the sun without sunscreen is harmful to your skin.

_____

Meaning: _____

4. I would like to visit the animals at the zoo weekly. _____

Meaning: _____

5. Meat seems to be a flavorful food for many dogs. _____

Meaning: _____

© Macmillan/McGraw-Hill

Name _____

A. Read the sentences. Then write each underlined word next to its definition below.

1. The author <u>observed</u> the silly things happening all around her.

2. Some would have been <u>discouraged</u> by the silliness, but she was not.

3. The silliness was <u>suitable</u> for someone writing a book of riddles.

4. Her editor <u>advised</u> the author about how to write a book of riddles.

5. She decided to <u>depart</u> for a vacation and finish the riddle book later.

6. The author had new ideas to <u>increase</u> the number of riddles.

   a. gave a suggestion or told someone   _____
      how to do something

   b. leave or go away   _____

   c. not hopeful   _____

   d. right for a certain purpose   _____

   e. saw and paid attention to   _____

   f. grow in number   _____

B. Use one vocabulary word in a sentence about riddles.

7. _____

    _____

CA R 1.0 Word Analysis, Fluency, and Systematic Vocabulary Development

The **plot** is the series of events that take place in a story.

The **setting** is where and when a story takes place. The setting is an important part of a story's plot development.

Read each story. Tell the plot and setting of each.

1. Tasha never wanted to try anything new. She refused every time she was asked. When Tasha went to school on Monday, her friends and teachers asked her to play on the school soccer team. Tasha was strong in sports, but she had never played soccer. She didn't want to try a new sport. Tasha knew that the school would get new gym equipment if the team was the best in the city. Tasha thought and thought about her fear of trying new things. Finally, she decided to play on the school soccer team. Her friends and teachers cheered.

Setting: _____

Plot: _____

_____

2. Mike loved attention. He always wanted everyone's eyes on him. Mike and his best friend, Eduardo, tried out for a play at a theater in town one Saturday. During the tryout they took turns asking and answering riddles. Mike knew Eduardo wanted a part in the play more than anything else. At first, Mike interrupted each time it was Eduardo's turn to talk. Then Mike saw how sad Eduardo looked. He stopped interrupting and let Eduardo say his lines. They both got parts in the play!

Setting: _____

Plot: _____

_____

As you read *One Riddle, One Answer*, fill in the Setting Web.

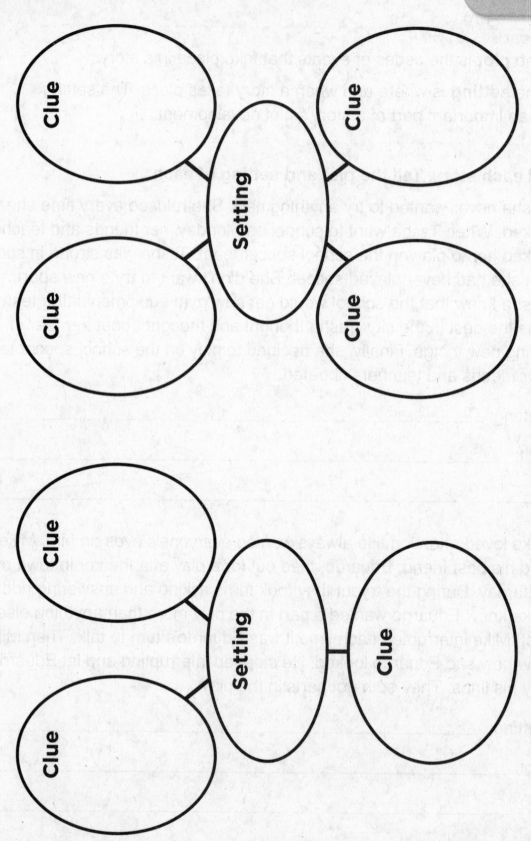

How does the information you wrote in this Setting Web help you understand plot development in *One Riddle, One Answer?*

Name _____

As I read, I will pay attention to phrasing and intonation.

	Once, long ago in Mexico, three brothers lived on a
10	small farm. The soil was rocky. There was not much rain.
21	Their crops did not grow well. For these reasons, they were
32	very poor.
34	Each day, Pablo, the youngest brother, got up before
43	sunrise. Then he crept silently out of the house while his
54	brothers, Manuel and Juan, snored. Pablo walked many
62	miles to the nearest school.
67	He couldn't spend the whole day at school, because he
77	had to return home to help his brothers on the farm.
88	"Here comes Mr. Smart Guy," Manuel would tease
96	Pablo when he returned. Manuel had never gone to school,
106	and he didn't want to go. He didn't understand why Pablo
117	liked it so much. 121

Comprehension Check

1. Why does Pablo get up before his brothers? **Plot Development**

2. Why does Manuel tease Pablo? **Plot Development**

	Words Read	–	Number of Errors	=	Words Correct Score
First Read		–		=	
Second Read		–		=	

© Macmillan/McGraw-Hill

R 1.3 Read aloud narrative and expository text fluently and accurately
and with appropriate pacing, intonation, and expression.

> **Sensory language** is a writer's use of words and images that appeal to the senses. Writers include strong adjectives, vivid verbs, and many details to help the reader understand how people or events in a story look, smell, sound, taste, or feel.

A. Choose a word or words from the box to add sensory language to each sentence. You do not need to use every word.

dark	green	frozen	cold	gigantic
friendly	terrified	kind	sad	big

1. The woods were _____.

2. The children felt _____.

3. Suddenly, a _____ bird appeared.

4. "Don't worry, I'll take you home," the _____ bird twittered softly.

B. Read the sentence below. Then describe what senses the writer is appealing to on the lines provided.

5. The gigantic bird tucked the children under its wings, soared above the clouds, and, when it reached their home, gently placed them on the ground.

_____

_____

_____

_____

© Macmillan/McGraw-Hill

CA R 2.0 Reading Comprehension

Name _____

When you read **unfamiliar words**, you can use many different kinds of clues to figure out what they mean. You can look at other words in the same sentence for clues. You can break a word into its parts to help you figure out the word's meaning. If these things don't help, you can look up an unfamiliar word in a dictionary.

Read each sentence. Figure out the meaning of the underlined word. Then write the correct meaning of the word.

1. I like riddles, but my sister tries to <u>pry</u> hints from Mom before she will guess the answer.

   Pry means _____.

2. That riddle is not <u>suitable</u> for young children.

   Suitable means _____.

3. The new <u>bedding</u> is much softer than the old bedding.

   Bedding means _____

   _____

4. Some whales are so <u>mammoth</u> that they grow to be over 100 feet long. Let's think of a riddle that uses this fact.

   Mammoth means _____

5. We read the <u>entire</u> book while we were at the library. We didn't know when we would be back again.

   Entire means _____.

R 1.6 Use sentence and word context to find the meaning of unknown words.

Using the Word Study Steps

1. LOOK at the word.

2. SAY the word aloud.

3. STUDY the letters in the word.

4. WRITE the word.

5. CHECK the word.
   Did you spell the word right?
   If not, go back to step 1.

X the Word

Put an X on the word that does not fit the pattern in each row.

1. careful	pitiful	barrel	bashful
2. harmful	panel	mindful	peaceful
3. helplessly	carefully	lovely	towel
4. peacefully	hopeful	carefully	beautifully
5. peaceful	helpless	speechless	sleepless
6. painless	priceless	rainless	peaceful
7. helplessly	money	happily	carefully
8. bubble	cheerful	helpful	peaceful
9. pitiful	colorful	careful	busily
10. rainless	priceless	pitiful	helpless

© Macmillan/McGraw-Hill

CA **LC 1.8** Spell correctly one-syllable words that have blends, contractions, compounds, orthographic patterns (e.g., *qu*, consonant doubling, changing the ending of a word from *-y* to *-ies* when forming the plural), and common homophones (e.g., *hair-hare*).

Name _____

A. There are six spelling mistakes in this paragraph. Circle the misspelled words. Write the words correctly on the lines below.

From behind the tree, the doctor observed the lion as he slept peacfully by the swamp. The doctor knew that even though the lion looked pieceful, he needed to get some very important medicine. To give the lion the medicine, the doctor would have to be very, very carefull. Lions do not like to be surprised. The shot would be paneless, though. Without it, the lion would be helples to fight the disease that was spreading in the jungle. The doctor knew he had a hard job. Yet it was important to him to have a job that was helpfull to animals.

1. _____   4. _____

2. _____   5. _____

3. _____   6. _____

B. Writing Activity

Write about a job in science you might want to have someday. Use at least three spelling words in your paragraph.

_____

_____

_____

_____

_____

_____

_____

LC 1.8 Spell correctly one-syllable words that have blends,
contractions, compounds, orthographic patterns (e.g., *qu*, consonant
doubling, changing the ending of a word from *-y* to *-ies* when forming
the plural), and common homophones (e.g., *hair-hare*).

One Riddle, One Answer
Grade 3/Unit 6
371

Two sentences can be combined by using an **adverb** from one of the sentences.
The butterfly lands on my finger. It lands **neatly**.
The butterfly lands **neatly** on my finger.

Combine each pair of sentences by using an adverb from one of the sentences. Write the new sentence on the line.

1. We enter the butterfly room.

We enter quietly.

_____

2. A butterfly brushes against my face.

It brushes gently.

_____

3. Tim reaches for a butterfly.

He reaches quickly.

_____

4. The butterfly darts away.

It darts speedily.

_____

5. The butterfly's wings echo through the room.

They echo softly.

_____

© Macmillan/McGraw-Hill

CA **LC 1.0** Written and Oral English Language Conventions

Name _____

- Two sentences can be combined by adding an **adjective** to one sentence.
- Two sentences can be combined by adding an **adverb** to one sentence.

A. Proofread the paragraph. Find and underline the pairs of sentences that can be combined.

    The butterfly swooped down from the sky. It swooped gracefully. It landed on Mom's lilac bush. It landed gently. It was a bush of purple lilacs. I walked over to it. I walked quietly. I wanted to see it up close. The butterfly was mostly yellow. It was a pale yellow. It had black marks around the edges of its wings. The wings looked like they were made of velvet feathers. They looked soft. I sketched the butterfly. I quickly sketched. Then I went inside and looked it up. It was a Tiger Swallowtail.

B. Writing Activity

Rewrite the paragraph with the combined sentences.

_____

_____

_____

_____

_____

_____

_____

_____

Name _____

Practice

Writing:
Character Development:
Shows Change and
Growth

1. **Think** of a time when you or someone you know changed the way he or she looked. **Write** that person's name:

_____

2. **Write** two to three sentences that show what the person looked like **before** the change.

_____

_____

_____

_____

3. **Write** two to three sentences that show what the person looked like **after** the change.

_____

_____

_____

_____

_____

_____

_____

_____

_____

_____

_____

_____

_____

© Macmillan/McGraw-Hill